THE GHOST OF LIBERACE

(NEW WRITING SCOTLAND 11)

L. F. Barton
ex suis libris
Edinburgh
June 1996

THE GHOST OF LIBERACE

(NEW WRITING SCOTLAND 11)

Edited by

A.L. KENNEDY
and
HAMISH WHYTE

with Meg Bateman (Gaelic Adviser)

Association for Scottish Literary Studies

Association for Scottish Literary Studies
c/o The Department of English, University of Aberdeen
Aberdeen AB9 2UB

First published 1993

ISBN 0–948877–18–9

The Association for Scottish Literary Studies acknowledges
with gratitude subsidy from the Scottish Arts Council

Typeset by Roger Booth Associates, Newcastle upon Tyne

Printed by BPCC-AUP Aberdeen Ltd.

CONTENTS

INTRODUCTION

At least one established writer did not submit work this year on the grounds that the anthology was not for oldies like him, a notion endorsed by at least one review. But *New Writing Scotland* is and always has been for new *writing*. Naturally, it also hopes to foster new writers, but not at the expense of 'old' ones. This year's issue, once again, mingles work from newcomers and old-timers.

If we must pick highlights, they might include Fred Urquhart's amusing and moving memoir of a gay menage, an affectionate portrait of post-war Fitzrovia and the writing life. We might mention James McGonigal's haunting weather sequence 'Approaching Spring', the memorably chilling Scots story 'The Rottans' Flittin' by Ronald W. McDonald and John Maley's title poem, an angry celebration of the new sexual realities. We are pleased to include contributions from two former editors, James Aitchison and Carl MacDougall and send congratulations to regular contributors Douglas Lipton and Irvine Welsh on the publication this summer of their first books.

NWS 11 is another varied and, we think, exciting lucky-bag of poems and stories. The usual human toing-and-froings are here, along with plenty of rats, fish, butterflies and foxes. Themes have emerged from the seemingly random editorial process – the city and the country; cafes, home and abroad; the pursuit of manly sports: and, of course, religion. Death and decay feature quite prominently in this number, but are laced with an often wicked humour and a strikingly mature social awareness. If *New Writing Scotland* could be considered as a snapshot of our national working psyche then we have more than a little cause for hope.

A.L. Kennedy
Hamish Whyte
August 1993

NEW WRITING SCOTLAND 12

Submissions are invited for the twelfth annual volume of *New Writing Scotland,* to be published in 1994, from writers resident in Scotland or Scots by birth or upbringing. Poetry, drama, short fiction or other creative prose may be submitted but not full-length plays or novels, though self-contained extracts are acceptable. The work must be neither previously published nor accepted for publication and may be in any of the languages of Scotland.

Submissions should be typed on one side of the paper only and the sheets secured at the top-left corner. Each individual work should be clearly marked with the author's name and address.

Submissions should be accompanied by two stamped addressed envelopes (one for a receipt, the other for return of MSS) and sent by 31 January 1994, to:

The Administrator, ASLS
c/o Dept of English
University of Aberdeen
Aberdeen AB9 2UB

Donald Adamson

PARTICLES

Archaeology seldom unearths a table.
The wood has burned or rotted,
the atoms have dispersed – some may be lodged in us.
We have, perhaps, some tableness in us.

And more. For where the metal detector bleeps
at a day configured by sun and cloud
like today, or a view we'd see
from our window, there's the dust
of principles worth dying and killing for,
an absolute tsardom, long reduced
to a democracy of indifference,
an equality of unconcern.

The smithereens float like wild-flower seeds,
tiny, barbed, catching in our clothes
and settling in our eyes: motes
like infinitesimal traffic lights,
winking red and green at us, infallibly
directing us to head-on collisions.

James Aitchison

THE VICTORY
(I.M. Alexander Scott, 1920–1989)

'"Done is a battle on the dragon black".'
You spoke as if the poet could win back
our nationhood, and the land's life or death
could be decided by the poet's breath:
Soutar, MacDiarmid, Henryson, Dunbar.

I pressed you once about your earlier war.
You waded through the dying and the dead
to reach the shore. Wounded, you would have bled
to death beside the men of your platoon
rather than give up the ground you'd won.

And when the enemy had you by the throat
at last, you joked in whispers and you fought
so long that by the end you'd found a way
of death that was another victory.

THRESHOLDS

To come in from the garden's summer light
and think you've crossed the threshold between sight
and nothingness because each room is blind
with smoke ... To wake up in the night to find
your pillow soaked with blood, your mouth, your nose
sticky with blood and yet to wonder whose
the blood can be ... To listen to the pitch
of your voice rising, breaking in a screech
of puny rage ... is to know these intense
wild bits and pieces of experience –
so vivid that they seem hallucinatory –
filed instantly as long-term memory.
And know year after year your mind will stage
black comedies of smoke and blood and rage.

THE INHERITANCE

The war, the hospitals – he was away
so long he was a stranger when he died;
I knew his face better from holiday
snapshots than from the life; and when I tried
to weep there were few tears. Later, I thought
I owed him part of my life for the years
he lost and for his early death. I ought
to have known that my father re-appears
in me no matter what I think: I feel
about books, craftsmanship, woodlands at dusk
just as he once did, his coded will
decoded as I sit here at my desk
translating impulses that might fulfil
my father's purpose and complete his task.

Lynne Bryan

FAMILY FEARS

I'm on the number 3 bus travelling from Five Oaks to Rozel. It is hot. The sun glares through the window. Sweat trickles from my armpits. I wipe the palms of my sticky hands on my shorts.

I'd like to move to a shadier spot, but the bus is packed. There's a queue of people standing in the gangway, all seats are occupied.

It's an unhappy bus load. Nobody smiles. Fathers whack their kids for whining. Mothers grimace. The two women in front argue bitterly. I clutch my stomach, made nauseous by pregnancy.

Rob sits next to me. He's pretending to be somewhere else. He gazes, blank-eyed, at the roof of the bus. He does not seem to notice my discomfort, and occasionally adds to it, moving his elbow to jab me in the side. I choose not to point this out. I don't want to get into one of our futile talks which go round and round in circles. I'm fed up with them. They exhaust me. Everything exhausts me.

I am eleven weeks pregnant. And from the day I conceived, though I had no idea I'd conceived, I've felt terrible. When I visited the Doctor's I cried, believing I had a fatal disease. He told me I was creating a new life, and that such work wouldn't come easy. He told me I'd get a break in the middle three months. The Honeymoon Period. I long for this time. I need space from the physical symptoms to think, and to reason with Rob.

The bus turns a sharp corner, narrowly missing a stone wall. 'Whoa...' cry the people in the aisle as they fall against each other. I smile, and look to see if Rob smiles too, but he continues to stare at the roof. He's as stubborn as the two women in front who, despite the commotion, still bicker.

The two women are sisters. There's no mistaking it. They dress differently, but their profiles are the same. They have hooked nose profiles, pointed chins, smallish foreheads, beady ferret-like eyes. They are sisters, but they behave like enemies. They scold and nip. They raise their hands, edging to slap.

Rob has three sisters. He has a photograph of them in his flat. They sit arm in arm on a flowery sofa. They look relaxed with each other, and happy. Rob loves his sisters. He loves his mum and dad. He kisses them hello. He kisses them goodbye. He shares everything with them. Already he has sent them postcards of Jersey Zoo, Grosnez Point and Rozel Harbour.

Rozel Harbour is one of the quieter bays in Jersey. The beach is stony which discourages many people, especially those who want to build sand castles. But I like it. I like it because it is quiet, and because it is charming. Small boats sit waiting for the tide to come in. Ducks and geese mingle with the seagulls, taking turns to float on the ocean, to march along the pebbles, to bathe in the warm water spilling from the hotel overflow. There is only the one hotel, a discreet stone affair. Next to it runs the causeway, and beyond the causeway a small row of wooden shanty shops, and cafes. We have been on holiday for a week, and for three days out of this week we have visited Rozel.

The bus backs into its lay-by and the driver signals for people to get off. The mothers and fathers and kids make their noisy way to the nearby pub. It is dinner-time. Everybody is hungry and thirsty. I point to the pub, but Rob shakes his head. He lifts my shopping bag on to his shoulder, and makes down the road to the beach. I follow him, hating my acquiescence.

We enter a small cafe on the sea front. Rob digs his hand into his trouser pocket, removes his wallet. I stand by his side, determined not to say the first word. He looks at me. 'What do you want?' he asks.

I smile. 'An orange juice, please.'

The woman behind the counter pours the juice. She wears a striped dress made out of stretch cotton. It clings to her big bones. She strikes me as sexy and I am jealous. I want to be that free with my body, to flaunt my flesh. Like I used to, before the baby took over.

My friends ask me why I'm keeping this baby, because I seem to resent it so. I tell them I'm keeping the baby because I can't imagine getting rid of it. I tell them a story about a girl I met at college who'd had an abortion at fifteen and still seven years later was lighting candles for the foetus, praying for forgiveness. I tell them I'm a coward and I'm mixed up.

I take the juice and move to a table, tucked into the far corner of the cafe. I want somewhere private, shaded. I want to be alone. Nausea still lines my throat. My stomach is shaken. And I feel defeated, my mind battered by Rob.

He paid for this holiday. When he waved the aeroplane tickets before me, he said, 'This is what we both need. Get us away from our jobs, get us away from the pressure. You'll see, a little bit of sun, a little bit of sand and things won't seem so bad.' I kissed him then. I believed he'd decided to give me what I most want – a break, a rest, time. I strapped myself into the aeroplane seat, watched home slide away, and felt so hopeful. But as soon as we got to the hotel, he started pestering me again.

We have been together for five years. Our relationship has been an unfettered one. He's lived on one side of town. I've lived on the other. It's suited me. It seemed to suit him. But now I'm pregnant and keeping the baby, he wants our lives to change. He wants me to live with him, to prepare a nest, to turn us into a family.

When I was fourteen mum, dad, my sister and I went to France. Our first holiday abroad. We stayed in a small white cottage, with terracotta roof tiles. The cottage was owned by a farmer. It sat on some coarse scrub. It had two bedrooms, a bathroom, and a large kitchen and living-room combined. The walls separating the rooms were made of a thin grey clay. You could hear everything. You could hear how quiet we were, how we never really spoke. One day my sister and I broke out. We danced around the kitchen to a French pop song blaring from the radio. We flung our arms about and laughed and shouted. 'Stop that,' said my mother, and we did. We spent the rest of the holiday sitting with our parents outside the cottage. My mother crocheted. My father slept. My sister and I read magazines. It was just how we behaved at home, except it was worse, heightened by being alone in the middle of a field, in the middle of a foreign country.

I sip the juice, watch the people outside the cafe. A small child, with a bucket and spade clutched in one hand, skips around the parked cars. The sisters from the bus wait for deckchairs. They flap at each other like agitated hens. Then the younger-looking one grabs the elder, pulls her arm roughly backwards and upwards into a half-Nelson.

'Did you see that?' I say to Rob, who plants himself opposite me.

'Not interested,' says Rob. He has bought himself a large bowl of multi-coloured ice-cream. Around the ice-cream runs a trail of chocolate sauce. He takes a scoop and pushes it into his mouth. He's feeling combative. I can sense he's decided today is the day.

I drain the glass of juice, avoid looking at him, stare at the milk machine. I watch the machine's stainless steel arm whip the white cool milk. 'You're not being fair,' I say.

'I'm not being fair!' Rob moves his head in front of the milk machine, so I have to look at him. Around his mouth is a line of pink and green ice-cream. Messy as a toddler.

'You've missed your mouth,' I say, pointing to his lips, but not touching his skin.

'God, Beth,' says Rob. He wipes a serviette over his face, smearing the ice-cream into his hairline. 'Why are you avoiding it?'

'It's in your hair now,' I say.

'Then you have it,' says Rob. He pushes his bowl of melted ice-cream towards me.

'It'll make me sick,' I say. I put my hands on the plastic cafe table, to lever myself out of my chair. 'Everything makes me sick.'

'Oh Beth,' says Rob. 'Please sit down. We have to talk.'

I stand up. 'I'm going for a walk,' I say. 'I need some fresh air.'

I leave the cafe, pass by the sisters who carry their deck chairs. The younger sister walks effortlessly, her muscled fist knotting her chair to her side. The elder sister struggles. She has tried to tuck her chair under her arm like a newspaper. But it's too heavy for her. It keeps slipping to drag along the road. I smile at her, and I think I hear her say 'It's not smiles I need.'

I head for the rocks lining the far side of the beach. The sun coats my shoulders, the back of my neck, as I walk down the causeway, tread the stony sand. I don't look behind me. I'm afraid Rob may be following. Pursuing me till he gets the response he wants.

I find a boulder, free from the slime of wet seaweed, and sit down. A seagull swoops to land close by. The sudden flap of wings startles me. I look up, register the bird's beaky face, its strange open eyes, somebody approaching. I expect Rob, and brace myself.

The younger sister places her deckchair on the solid sand fronting my rock and kicks at the gull. 'Woo. Woo,' she shrieks. The gull rises into the air, hooting sharply. 'Nasty things,' she says.

She erects her chair, patting the stripy canvas with her hands. I watch her stocky body as it moves around the chair. She is dressed in a long sleeved T-shirt, brown knitted leggings. Sweat shimmers on her face. She removes her shoulder bag, and places it on the seat of her chair. 'Constance,' she shouts. 'Hurry up.'

Her elder sister picks her way through the sleeping sunbathers. A middle-aged man in beige shorts carries her chair. He reminds me of Rob's father. Guileless. Kind. He wears a bemused smile and a floppy beach hat.

I once went for a drink with Rob's father. It was a cold wintry day. We sat huddled together on a bench in a local pub. I can't remember how we came to be there, alone. Rob probably arranged it, as he arranged my bowling trip with his sisters, my sauna with his mother. Rob wants me to get along with his family. And I do. I enjoyed sipping my beer, listening to his father tell his tales. It was like listening to a story on the radio, a story told in comforting tones about sleepy lives and endless good times. He told me about his childhood, just after the war, when he swam in the village pond using his sister's knickers for trunks. He told me about his mother's enormous bust, the way she tried to hide it under large shapeless aprons. Then he wanted to know about my father, and I had to say there's nothing to tell, we went on holidays and he slept and we waited to come home. Rob's father thought I was joking. He winked at me, like Rob often winks at me. 'Oh come on now,' he said.

'Constance,' screeches the younger sister. 'Where did you put the suntan cream? Don't tell me you've forgotten to pack it? Constance!'

She stands over her sister's chair. I watch as she wraps her sturdy hands around the wooden frame. She tugs, but Constance digs her heels into the sand, nestles her bony bottom deep into the chair and refuses to answer. 'Constance,' screeches the younger sister. 'Constance!'

I feel sorry for these sisters. They fight over the smallest things. The younger sister pummels at Constance, her whole body desperate to knock through their differences. But Constance seems resigned, disposed to sit it out. She reminds me of my parents, passively waiting.

Last summer I was miles away from my parents. Miles away from my sister and the nervous shake of her hands.

Miles away from the memories.

I turn from the sisters, try to concentrate on a speed boat breaking out of the harbour. A white speed boat with a flash of silver and the name 'Princess' painted on its prow. I imagine I see the French coastline, and maybe I do. A grey streak on the horizon. Enticing.

Rob laughed when I first told him I wanted to escape, to pack my bags and flee. He said his mother had felt the same through all her pregnancies. Hormonal, he said. Natural. Then he stopped laughing. Because it's so obvious I'm not his mother. Because it's so obvious I'm frightened. 'But you can't avoid the family,' he argued. 'You're having a baby. A baby is family.'

The hotel gong sounds. Lunch is done. It alarms the ducks treading the hotel wall. It alarms me. The dull note threads through my nausea, makes my body stiffen, my legs swing. My legs are a reminder of my childless days. They are thin, free-looking. I envy them.

I watch a small group of people leave the hotel, walk through the gap in its wall on to the beach. I see Rob standing near the wall. His hands are raised, shielding his eyes from the sun. He searches for me.

I trace the outline of his body, witness his solid shape. He is not like me. I knew that when we first met. It wasn't important then.

He finds me and lifts his hand to wave. I wave back. Then signal for him to stay where he is. Him at one end of the beach, me at the other. With a fresh salty breeze blowing between us.

Ron Butlin

THIS YEAR

1

As the days grew shorter we'd sing our way home through
the darkness
– your voice in front, mine half a beat behind.
Trees clawed at us and the wind hissed
– I held your coat tight.

2

This year we keep to the concrete path round the building.
Tea and biscuits in your room. A bed, a chair, radio,
some photographs – you say you've everything you need.

Another day has passed, another evening. I'll leave soon.
I have to. When the trees press too close our hands touch:

There is no singing, no road home.

Jacqueline Cameron

HAIKUS IN FRANCE

SMOKE

Paris was a whirl
In the cafes, in the bars
I searched for beautiful people
There were none
In the coffee aroma and the Gauloises' haze
They hid

NOISY

We'll have to shut the windows tonight
If we're going to get any sleep

KISS ME

A cat stalked the aisles of the cathedral
You wouldn't kiss me in there
If a cat can run in a cathedral
Then why can't you kiss me?

CRASH

When the plane tucked up its legs
And leapt into the air
I knew we would plummet like a stone
Instead, we drank champagne
And ate barley sugar

Robert Crawford

FLIGHT

First meeting with Dr Spreadsheet
I was weighed down with my tax returns, but he
Just levitated, floating across the ceiling like a leaf

From Steven Spielberg, out through the open french windows.
I huffed after, below him as he buzzed car roofs
In the Pay and Display. I pulled the choke, jumped

A red light. A fly buzzed in my inner ear,
'Things will be different. Your scruples are ballast. Trust me –'
'Dr Spreadsheet,' I yabbered, 'is that you talking?'

Couldn't see his face, only the criss-cross soles
Of his Doc Martens, and the dark ovals of his trouser leg ends
As he went headfirst, horizontal, like the breath of autumn's
being

Or a contour-hugging missile, skimming a row of shops.
Then it struck me – that pistol I'd found by X-rays
In Joe's stomach in the morgue was Dr Spreadsheet's

And this was how he paid back those corporate lawyers
Who'd proven him innocent. Guilt brought him man powered
flight,
Patented, saleable. My red-eyed years at the workstation

Weren't worth a rat's fart now, his chunky soles told me,
Looping the loop, then zooming away like Stealth.
I crossed the hard shoulder, laid my head to the wheel,

Crying a bit at my effort all airbrushed out,
And a bit with relief cos the effort could stop now he'd cracked
it.
Back at Plodco, still munching on ways of escape,

I loiter offscreen while ABC, BBC pan up
As he hovers over them, mouthing, 'So What? The gun was mine,
But I rose above it,' while the press stargazes

Gawkily, serving him up hot to readers
Choking in Motherwell, syndicating him on
To Canberra and Singapore as he smiles down into my hair,

'No worries. You could all do this.'

THE GAELIC CARIBBEAN

for Fred D'Aguiar

I want the silence to be broken,
Then unbroken, healing around you.

A boat noses into Barra,
Volleyed by the Atlantic, anachronistic.

People are battened in its hold, speaking
Spanish-Gaelic – cleared, aborted

Mixed infants, their parent language
The torn-out tongues of America.

A boat noses into Barra
So shot-up it will stay

Anchored in long stories and heather roots,
A Cree boat, a Nevis boat, a vessel

Filled with everything spilt. Mama Dot
Will croon in Gaelic and Guyanese Gaels

On their plantations of drowsy peat
Unslave themselves to listen.

Cortez is giving way to St Brendan.
All night a woman cries

Something island, a Creole
Clearing word that dismisses the silence

Then whistles it back like a shepherd calling
His lost black dog from the seaweed.

Lizbeth Gowans Daly

SCRAPS

Ella had two treasured pictures in her keeping. One was a postcard of a sleeping black gypsy in the desert with a huge lion bending over him. She'd once stared long at this one and finally figured out that, in the wild, sleep must be a sacred protection, and so the sleepers are safe. She was glad she'd made that sense of the picture.

The other one was a photograph of two soldiers. This one had had no mystery to it until now, and she thought she would never understand it however long she stared.

They're not relatives of ours, she told herself, to keep at a distance the two soldiers now come to stay on leave. Even the lassies they're going to marry aren't relatives. They're adopted. And it wasn't even a close relative that adopted them. Just a second cousin of a second auntie.

But it didn't work, didn't make her feel less ashamed, and could not wipe out the sad disbelief, most of all the anger. And to think how she'd longed to meet them, looked forward to their coming, to admiring in the flesh what she had only gazed at in the photograph of them in their uniforms leaning against a tank. Their wide grins and crinkly eyes looked full of fun, quite entrancing and, she'd thought, terribly brave there against the ruins of a bombed building.

Regardless of their correct cadre, the bairns in the family had taken to calling them 'the Commandos', and so they went on being so called by everyone. It was 'The Commandos are coming for a week's leave' or 'Here's a postcard from the Commandos', and once, when the German prisoners-of-war were spoken of kindly (for hadn't they made splendid wooden toys for the estate children at Christmas?), someone said, 'Ye better no let the Commandos hear ye talkin' like that.'

The precious week's leave was nearly over, with only two more days left. To Ella it felt like two months. She was sure that if only they could be gone, out of her sight and hearing, she would be all right again.

'What are ye daein' up there? You leave thae aipples alane.'

Her father passed below the branches where she'd found

refuge from the rest, a favoured place in times of hurt.

'I'm no touchin' the apples,' she shouted back, thinking of his own boastful stories of boyhood raids on the schoolmaster's trees.

As he walked on he instructed her, 'Aye, weel, if it's trees ye're wantin' tae sclim, get up in that elderberry for your mother. She's wantin' tae mak anither pail o' the wine.'

She knew that. The Commandos had nearly finished the old. Ella thought it a terrible concoction. The very smell coming off yon dark red stuff with the toast slices floating on top was enough to send her reeling off clutching her stomach at the best of times. Now it was worse since she'd seen them lifting it in glass jars, purple red, to their mouths, like... She shut her eyes tightly, holding onto the branch to keep down the rising sick, whispering 'gentle Christ Jesus'. It was her swear word, her prayer, and her blessing, depending on how the world was behaving. Often, like a lullaby from babyhood, the words comforted. Gentle, gentle, gentle...

It was her own fault for being within earshot, of course. If she'd only done what she'd been told and gone to help Will and Christine look after the young ones across the field near the fast-flowing river, the thing wouldn't have happened. But the company of a mere brother and cousin was no match for the snatches of conversation to be collected within a carefully chosen radius of the chaffing adult group with, always, the Commandos at the centre.

It was easy to seem not listening, not remotely interested, to be fully engrossed in cleaning up an old pram for the play of wee Jean.

From her eyrie she could hear a commotion from over by the river. She craned to see. Oh aye, the Commandos again, so welcomed into the play of the young ones. She could see them in their dress uniforms, one of them flinging Jean about his shoulders to the sound of her screaming laughter. Just yesterday she too would have hung on their horse-play like that, taken their big hands, pulled them away for walks, and basked in their pleasure at being here 'away from the fray', as they put it, and among their own good folk. The swift feeling of loss hurt her middle again. Gentle, gentle...

Over and over, she wondered why they had needed to mention it at all, to anybody. It was the kind of thing that should be kept dark, for ever and ever. And yet, the thought of them striding about the countryside, being so liked by everybody, young and old, and especially by such as herself, and nobody having any idea of what they had done, made her feel very queer. It was like that daft question she'd heard of – if a tree falls in the forest and nobody sees or hears, has it really happened?

In fact, the rest of the adults who heard the story had treated it as just another wartime scrape. But she knew it wasn't. And something else, too, she knew. For all the rest of them had responded as if to a crazy prank, Ella was sure they only did it because the Commandos were their visitors. Not a single word of blame could be spoken or even looked. It was like a kind of natural forgiveness.

Endlessly, she kept hearing that bit in the talk where it seemed to get louder. Or clearer. Or was it that everyone else had become silent, letting those few sentences stand out, making her look up and see the gesture that had destroyed her peace forever?

> *We came on them at daylight. Dead to the world, the three o' them in the ruin. They never stirred. No even when Bull...*
>
> The swift click of tongue and the forefinger across the throat took over from words... *the yin in the middle. Tae gie the other two the fricht o' their lives when they woke up, he said. Helluva bugger, Bull. Yin o' them that disny look forward tae amnesty. No like us, eh?*

They made it sound like they were in the clear, but their strange laughing as they said it came across otherwise. After all, they had been there, comrades, collaborators altogether.

She could still see them playing with the bairns by the river, behaving like big bairns themselves. Their carefree laughter carrying across the field sounded stupid to her now. They *were* stupid. They didn't, for one thing, seem to know the difference between armistice and amnesty. She did. And, under her breath, she'd told them. 'You mean *armistice*,' she'd said, with all the weight of her shock and contempt behind the words, but keeping her face bent on the work of rubbing hard the spokes of the pram. Nobody, it seemed, had paid her any attention, children at such times being very definitely seen and not heard. So there was no satisfaction, no relief, in letting the famous Commandos know how stupid *she* thought them, if no one else did.

And now it was her that was the banished one, hidden here in the branches, rocking the pain that wouldn't sleep now, not if she gentled Jesus till the kye came home. For now her mother was angry with her.

'Away ye go wi' the Commandos, Ella. They're gaun a walk tae the falls wi' the bairns. Lee that auld pram alane. Whit's wrang wi' ye the day? Ye ken ye like gaun wi' them. They were askin' whit way ye're stayin' hame an' no gaun wi' them. Why no?'

'Because!' she burst out. 'Just because!'

'Because whit?'

'Because... they're full o' theirsels a' the time. An' they've nae right, because they're just ignorant, an' stupid, an'... I hate them baith... an'...'

The slap stopped her instantly. 'Never you talk like that, Ella Yuill. You have no idea. You think because... You think because you heard... Listen, my lady, to me. You don't know what...' Then the fire had died down in her mother's broken words and at last all she said was 'They're just poor scraps o' laddies come back frae the war. An' you watch your clever tongue wi' them. Mind me, now!'

She followed the movement of the group by the river and held her breath. One was still with the bairns, but the other was hastening towards the house. She watched him. He slowed, seemed to droop, then came on haltingly until, beneath her tree, he threw himself down on his back, with his arms crossed high across his neck, hands clasping shoulders, like someone cold.

He was so close she could see where the sweat darkened his hair around the temples. She stared at the chest of his tunic as it moved with his breathing. Gentle, gentle... Don't sleep. The desert gypsy...

She waited in distress, convinced she'd never move an inch without disturbing him. What if one of the apples chose to snap clear of its drying leaf-heart and fall on him, like Newton's? The gravity of that possibility, of him looking up and finding her looking down, watching him, sent her mind flying for excuses. No use. Suddenly desperate to move, she turned softly to change foothold and handhold, but nervousness made her feel clumsy and unlucky. She steadied herself, waiting.

Suddenly she saw that Will had crept up and was clearly

about to hurl himself playfully onto the sleeping soldier. She tried to call a warning to her brother not to do it, but was too late. He leapt onto the chest of the soldier who rolled to his feet roaring the name of his pal. Then his body's blind stagger turned instantly, and still blindly, into a readying of forces to counter-attack. The blindness and the roaring of him terrified her, but she could not move. She crouched in the tree, blinking at the inevitability of a body building up to violence, against her brother.

Then, in a rush, the other one was there between them and the roaring faltered. 'It's a' right, Norrie. Norrie, Norrie! Calm doon, man. Ye're a' right. Ye're at hame.'

They were struggling and holding onto each other, the Norrie one, no longer blind, crying now like a hurt bairn. His pal turned his head to a stricken Will and the rest of them standing there watching. 'Away ye go hame,' he said. 'Norrie here's no very weel. Go an' tell yer mammie tae pit the kettle on, eh?'

Wee Jean nodded understandingly. 'Wull I tell her tae get doon the syrup o' figs? That's whit she gies us.'

His voice quavered as he replied. 'Aye, hen. You dae that.' He spoke to the Norrie one's face still hidden in his shoulder. 'Ye fancy some syrup o' figs, Norrie? Eh? Wee Jean here's offerin'.'

Slithering down quickly from the branches to round up the young ones and get them home, Ella heard the Norrie one's great gasp of indrawn breath and the tearful words as he let it out. 'Aye, a' right. Seein'... she's offerin'.' The next thing was the Commandos staggering about together under the apple branches, laughing like bairns being tickled till it hurt.

They said they would better leave after their tea, restless, it seemed, to move on to other relatives. They appeared pre-occupied at the last, even indifferent to the bairns, yet Ella felt both of them, at different moments, turn their eyes from their plates to watch her as she moved from hob to table helping to serve the family. The strain of not looking at them nearly made her chuck the teapot onto the floor and run.

When they had been waved off on the bus at the roadend, Ella's mother turned to her frowningly. 'Did you say onythin' tae thae laddies? Eh?'

'No.'

'So whit happened tae Norrie ower in the field? I ken

somethin' happened.'

Ella wanted badly to say what was always the safest, that she didn't know, wasn't sure, couldn't say. Some of that was true. She was just beginning to know, wasn't sure of her own position now, and certainly didn't feel like putting any of it into words.

'He went to sleep under the apple tree and I think,' she said, 'he had a sort of nightmare.'

It seemed to pacify her mother who linked arms with her as they walked home. Later, for her own pacification, like saying her 'gentle Christ Jesus' when she was young yesterday, she took a square of coloured cardboard from her cupboard and made a design round the edge on both sides. Then, using her best script, she wrote on one side the word *armistice*. Turning the card over, she wrote *amnesty*, and put it away for the future.

John Duffy

TEARDROP

There were questions that hadn't formed
during the pregnancy: would the juke box
have to go from the bedroom,

for example? He had glumly redecorated
the box room; his ears reddened
at the certainty of colleagues'

You'll be hoping for a boy. Would he
become the man he didn't want to be?
Football: guns: keeping a hard edge.

He learned breathing, relaxation
at classes, watched the women
converge, the men sidle towards or away

from one another; told the group
I'm not sure I want this baby.
Christine knew. He knew she wouldn't

try to talk him round. Not him.
Not her. They loved the gleaming chrome,
the whirr; the purr; the throb from the big

bright pink flashing machine, black sheen
in the corner, thrashing out **Tears**
on my pillow; I cry myself to sleep.

The harsh hospital light is no place
for tender things – sharp smells; and green masks,
in charge, but edgy. They know

about labour, they don't know Christine.
He looks in her eyes; she's there, behind
sweat, grunts: alone in the back of her head.

The masks eye digits, blips, he puts his arm
round her shoulders, his mouth by her ear:
Use the muscles above, relax below.

Be the shape of a teardrop. Broadening
out from a sharp point, she opened
like springtime; the slow coming

to the moment of a sudden
sliding rush, and nothing has been
as real as this love is sweat, is

tears, is the unimagined heat
from the baby, or the distance the three
of them make from the midwives, the world.

SURFACE TENSION

Beside the reservoir
I lean
into sun, wind,

the rustle of summer
grasses, the hiss
of motorways. The town below

is Saturday
washing lines
and frantic

barking. Up here
there's a skylark,
level with my eye –

which centres
the bird
on Cnoc a Mhadaid,

fifteen hundred feet
high, and twenty miles
down river. Unimpressed

by my perspective,
the lark goes on
improbably

balancing on a cone
composed of pure
boastfulness,

one
hundred and
fifty feet high,

solid
as any hillside.
On the water,

a fly tilts
over mountainous
ripples, places

each foot
in a foot-shaped
dimple.

Gavin Ewart

A 19th CENTURY ADOLESCENT REBEL TIME-TRAVELS TO 1992

('The Campbells Are Coming')

I want to be a sot and thrall of lust
I want to be a throt and Saul of lust
I want to stroke a bosomy beauty's bust

I want to be beaten by
I want to be eaten by

Marlene Dietrich
Cheryl Campbell
Cheryl Campbell
Cheryl Campbell
Cheryl Campbell
Cheryl Campbell*

* insert any other names that seem desirable

[Oh, the sots and thralls of lust
Do in spare hours more thrive than I that spend,
Sir, life upon thy cause. – G.M. Hopkins]

WAVERLEY

Young likely lad, Ed Waverley –
not trained armily or navally –
was brought up by some old Scots silver spoons,
he never was pedantic
but poetic and romantic,
till he was made a Captain of Dragoons.

Free from all malaise and malice,
he met cultured Rose[1], then Alice[2]
(a bosomy girl, and wrapped up in a plaid,
a daughter of the Highlands
and not much like Dadie Rylands[3])
but he met his match in Flora[4] – what a maid!

She was quite a girl, that Flora –
how could he *not* be an adorer? –
a Jacobite to the pants she didn't wear
(when Romantic love-light flickers
no romantic girl wears knickers –
and no one, then, had ever seen a pair!).

She'd not alter her position –
though he gave up his commission
in the service of the second King called George –
there was, sure, no alteration
though they had an altercation
in a very picturesque and rocky gorge...

Skilful Gilfilan[5], Davie Gellatley[6] –
not in Birmingham or Batley
would you find such canny (or such idiot) Scots –
nor could Horace Annesley Vachell[7]
delineate Aunt Rachel
or the hardy whisky-drinking Highland sots.

But it's Rose was the outsider
and quite a skilful rider...
she came up in his affections. At the post
he preferred her tender feelings
as she raised her eyes to ceilings –
her devotion was the thing that mattered most!

Now the Forty-Five was brewing,
all the patriots were queueing,
hotpot Fergus and the formal feudal Baron,
Violent Vic[8] and Don Green Bean[9],
they were seething round the scene
like the molten metal at the ironworks (Carron)[10].

Fergie's Bailie, old Macwheeble,
he alone seemed weak and feeble –
but not the frisky risky Callum Beg,[11]
Vic's fresh servant; hunting, fishing,
when the claymores started swishing,
he was never loth to shake a leg!

Preston to Pinkie-house. Victorious Scots
marched with some glory (some think lots)
for young Charles Edward Stuart, the Pretender.
Ed fought there; but soon Culloden[12]
was dismal news, and newly sodden
with all the blood the clans could bravely render!

So rebellion's voice grew muted,
fiery Ferg was executed –
but the Baron (lucky dog) restored and spared.
Rosie got what she had merited –
all his lands, which she inherited,
and the bliss which she and Ed quite rightly shared!

Flora mourned her warrior brother –
she would never be a mother,
for she found a convent and became a nun,
in a dark religious gloom
she forsook the drawing-room
and all elegant behaviour in the sun!

Notes: If anyone thinks these Notes are excessive, they should consult Sir Walter Scott's original *Waverley*, where every kind of Note, Introduction, Preface, Anecdote and Appendix is to be found (in the Penguin edition).

1. Rose Bradwardine, daughter of the Baron of Bradwardine.
2. The wild but beautiful daughter of Donald Bean Lean.
3. Once the renowned Master of King's College, Cambridge. Famous as an English scholar and producer of Shakespeare's plays.
4. Sister of Fergus Mac-Ivor Vich Ian Vohr, the Chief of Clan Ivor.
5. A very puritanical Presbyterian.
6. A simpleton, regarded as a 'natural' but perceptive, like a Shakespearean fool, employed as a jester by the Baron.
7. Horace Annesley Vachell at about the turn of this century wrote a school story called *The Hill*, about Harrow.
8. Vich Ian Vohr was the clansmen's name for Fergus Mac-Ivor.
9. Donald Bean Lean (pronounced Bane Lane) was the head of a robber band and very unreliable.
10. The Carron Ironworks near Falkirk were famous.
11. In the novel Callum Beg is suspected of taking a pot-shot at Waverley.
12. The decisive English victory of the Duke of Cumberland, still famous for his cruelty ('the butcher Cumberland').

Donald Farquhar

PEE-THE-BEDS

Peerie flouers, yalla flouers
raxed aroun ma taes.
The pyntin blades were emerant ure
an heicher nor the gress.
The yalla heids turnt tae the east
tae tryst the dawin sin.
Pee-the-beds were warmin herts
that steikit for the mune.
Syne the day the sin wins oot
the taps are yoke tae flee.
A blawed a fuff atween ma haun
tae coont the sodgers by.
Thair taes in saun like blawin seed
thair heids cramasie, ay.

TEETHLESS

Open wide nou.
aaaaaa.
Open a bit mair.
Awwwww.
Wide open nou Sir.
aaaaaaa.
See us a langer drill hen.
Wide nou Sir.
Awwwwwww.
Wider!
AAAaaaaa.
Birrrr.
Birrrrr, birrrr. Snap!
Aww Aww Aww Awwwwww!
The drill broke Sir.
Eeeeeeee.
Jist relax nou Sir.
aaaaaaa.
Jist anither wee jag Sir.
Awwwww.
Get big Effie hen
this will tak the twa o us.
Aw Aw Aw Awwwww.
Richt Effie haud his heid.
Open up nou Sir.
AAAaaaaa.
Wider Sir.
Awwwwww.
Jist relax Sir.
This will no hurt?
AAEEEEE EEEECH!
Nearly there Sir.
Aww Aww Aww Awwwwww Awwwwww.
Open wide nou!
AAAAaaaa AAAAaaaa.
Haud ticht nou Effie.
EEEE EEEECH Awwaaa.
That's it Sir,
pey at the desk.

Raymond Friel

DAUGHTER

Four mannequin brides, arranged in Indian file.
Poor creatures, they have no-one to give them away.

Your hood up, you focus firmly on the dresses,
Not the alien-dead eyes, the tear-streaked window.

I think of your father, indulgent beside you
On Pembroke High Street some drizzly Saturday.

Is that what governs a daughter's idea of men?
Would he and I have got on like a house on fire?

He left you once before: driving Llewellwyn's bus
To Madras (what with work being scarce), bed-ridden

By a vindaloo the day he got there. Like me,
He had to get his twenties out of his system.

THE BOAT HOUSE AT LAUGHARNE

A plummy Charles Laughton voice
(A late recording)

Inhabits the low-beamed
Cabin of a front room.

A Fern Hill tea-towel wrinkles
Over the hearth.

'He was a right bastard to his wife,'
You said, and left.

Outside, I peered into the writing shed:
Cut off, cosy;

From the rickety desk, a dazzling view
Of the Towy estuary;

Postcards of poets on the lintel,
A Van Gogh chair;

Scrunched up papers by the stove
For the credulous,

As if he'd chucked it and headed off
For a swift one...

Below, you picked your way carefully
Over the rocks.

Robin Fulton

A CLEAR START TO THE DAY

The sun that has reached Finland is not
yet here: here we have Norwegian pre-
dawn steel brightness
I look for and find Japanese-like
signs black on silver so razor-edged
I can't read them

The sycamore has lost all its leaves
but clutters the sky with black-winged seeds
that won't let go
The sky is cluttered also by crows
a creaking armada that lasts two
minutes, is gone

I carry that taint of clarity
into the day's tunnel whose colours
go wet and run
I have something sharp to interpret:
crows that have forgotten how to fly,
seeds that have flown

UTOPIAS

I spend a measured part
of my one measured life
crossing the many lives
of waves that elude me

There is no horizon
only a place where eye-
sight stops, a ring that keeps
me at its blind centre

A birch-tree would tell me
how fast I was passing
or with its shadow-hand
how long I was standing

If we could arrange for
birches on the North Sea
in return the hard miles
on home rock might relent

William Gilfedder

THE BIG CITY

I am not the poet of the fields and open spaces
Let me be seen drinking in a pub
The table littered with empty glasses
It may not be as healthy or as cheap
But it sure as hell makes you feel a damn sight better
And even if I don't get to become Poet Laureate
I can always spend a day in the country
It may not have the same attraction for me as the big city
But then again everyone to their own thing
I don't think living in the country's all it's cracked up to be
anyway
There's more going on in a city at the weekend
Than there is in the country all the year round
And you don't have to get up at five o'clock in the morning
To do it either
And another thing when the lights are fading and the country
folk
Are settling down for the night
The big city is just coming to life
And you know what that means
All you need is a few quid
A clean suit and you're off into the traffic
Man it's a rare feeling
There's nothing like it on earth
It's like working for the gaffer all week
And suddenly waking up and finding you're your own boss
Even the traffic lights are in your favour
Just waiting for you to make your move.

Jim Glen

EXCAVATIONS

Tommy brings his find up to my desk
for a less-than-expert evaluation,
a coin he's dug up near the embankment.
Blackened now and worn thin yet I can see
it's nothing more than a threepenny bit,
but of course he's never seen such a coin before
and so he thinks it could be Roman.
Still, he's been digging up the past right enough.

I think of the day in Halls when Marie told me of her life
in the time it took to make a batch of popcorn,
real American popcorn, the first I'd ever tasted.
I learned how her rich parents mailed her cheques
to stay away, but she was content she said,
measuring out her days from dig to dig.
'Not a real archaeologist,' she confessed,
'Just one of the brush-and-trowel brigade.'

I suppose if I'd been older or feeling less
of a 'hick from the sticks' I might have asked her out,
(the thought of strolling along Great Western Road
beside that dark-eyed Brooklyn blonde) but I didn't
and paid for my lack of temerity by spending the day
in Glasgow alone, feeling I'd swallowed a sack of confetti.
And paying for it again, it seems, with Tommy's coin
that might have been Roman but isn't.

John Glenday

FLOOER O SCOTLAND

Ower saft i the pow for the thistle
(Though we're jaggie enough bedtimes).

Ower coorse for the rose
(thank christ). Ower smaa for the pine.

Ower radge for the lily's chastity
an the orchid's miles too rare.

Bog cotton's for us, wha governs
the moss wi his ain heid on a spear.

Rody Gorman

DONAIDH

'S lìonmhaire na mairbh na na beò.
Tha 'n àireamh dhiubh daonnan a' dol am meud.
Nuair a chaochail thu 'n-uiridh (mòr am beud!)
Thog thu ort dhachaigh à Eilean an Sgleò
A ghlanas tìde (ciamar a tha i agaib'-pèin?)
A shluigeas do chainnt ghlan ann an cànan cèin.

Translation

DONNIE

The dead are more plentiful than the living.
Their number is always increasing.
When you died last year (more's the pity!)
You took off homewards from the Misty Isle
Which time and weather will erode (how is it with yourselves?)
And swallow your beautiful words into an alien language.

Stanley Roger Green

NO RETURN TO EDEN

No delegated angel person will loiter
On sentry duty at open rusting gates,
The garden now sublunary, a heritage park
Where forbidden fruit is served with cream.

Lacking the bite of burnt fossil fuels
Amaranthine fragrance would make us gag,
Lotus on nicotined palates would cloy,
The contrived tableaux of panther and fawn
Might suggest the use of sedative darts.

Doom-conditioned nerves need fiercer thrills –
Banner headlines presaging Armageddon,
Cramping our guts with iron as statesmen
Fulminate from safe debating chambers;
The dubious ambivalence that follows détente.

And how would we fill the nights in Eden
When not outstared by telly's Medusoid eye?
Dawn would find us combing the forest
For serpents to whet new perilous appetites.

And if a somnolent Jehovah drove us out,
Hurling thunderbolts inexpertly, we'd smile,
Knowing they were made from papier mâché.
And off we would saunter, wearing exile
Jauntily, like a tourist's sombrero.

Richard Hammersley

COMMUTING BACK TO HEATHROW AIRPORT

the worn old train was dust
it fluttered above South London
in the damp heat sweat stuck
my shirt to the seat of dust
below buildings were falling
and building at the speed of earth
prim landscapes were bursting
out of back gardens along the track
a great copper beech once
a focal feature of a lawn was
bending a fence and smothering
the weeds beneath it dog roses
competed for track side
with hedge bindweed
pink petals with a daub
of yellow stamens white trumpets
a bower for not sleeping
the train creaked
over beautyless drab terraces
the white man leaning on a sill
had dreadlocks 'Pay no Poll Tax'
the bill was on recycled paper
in another garden a ragged wash
fluttered over rusted old things
nettles and much more bindweed
creeping into Clapham station
there is a green gap by the track
where some industry fell down
or had been pushed aside
bindweed yet hardly hedges the wire
fence through which I see
a grand red and dun dog fox
digging for worms or beetles
paws pushing at the soil
panting for his city livelihood
the meaningless train pulls me away
to hesitate for no reason outside Victoria

Andrea Joyce

SHOT

When we first saw them
their fox spirits had already gone
though something lean and dark lingered on
under the heavy trees.

They lay together as never before
bodies crossed, feet bound,
stiff fur paling to creamy bellies
slung down on the brilliant ground.

Later beyond disgust
you stirred the living broth
of deliquescent fox
and heard a sound

like a tiny clattering sigh
an empire of maggots
born for a day
working to efface forever

the distinction between
one animal and another
making a dog and vixen
earth and flesh

all things the same.

Douglas Lipton

PRIMARY 6: THE SHOES

What beast ever had skin as thick
as the Scottish Lowland Aurochs,
the flesh-eating ox of the Clyde –
long-extinct, slaughtered by geography?
Rough blankets of its pelt
were dragged from the slaister
near Gowkthrapple,
and shears of carbo-tungsten steel
developed to carve them
into malleable sheets
of a leather the like of which
was never worked before.

Upstairs, in the drawing-office,
The Shoes took seven weeks of planning
by the hide-bound draftsmen,
who pored over boards and templates
into the hurricane-lamp lit
wee small hours.
Construction took eighteen months,
drums of sweat and shovelfuls of grime
of a hundred men in the shed,
using awls tipped with molybdenum
and lingel of ship-rat gut.

The launch on the Fairfield's slipway
was by Lady Strathbungo,
before a crowd of near-hysterical
fans of cordinering,
souters and their families,
invited guests from Italy,
local kids and teachers
on their worst behaviour,
freed from school.
'I name these shoes "Eumenides".
May God bless them
and all who walk in them.'

There was commentary
from the man himself
– Mr Dimbleby –
conveying every inch of The Shoes'
encroachment on the old slow river,
elaborating every Ooh and Aah
of the jamboree in the shipyard
for a nation's wireless audience
riveted to a million sets,
until, like a catamaran from the underworld,
The Shoes sat on the troubled water.
It was said that the tide in the Firth
rose two more feet that afternoon
before stability was restored.

My dad sold his sketch by Muirhead Bone,
his stamp collection with first-day covers,
his coins and booty from the War
and Joseph Conrad first-editions,
and bought them – The Shoes:
the pair of a lifetime.
I'd grow into them, eventually,
and never out of them.
For their preservation:
trees of ironwood
to keep their shape;
a daily burnishing of Kiwi Black
into the vamps and tongues;
and a smoker's toothbrush,
kept below the sink,
to scrub the mud from the welts
at the end of the Primary day.
Then he took his ball-pene
to the last in the shed
and drove a parapet of segs
around their heels and soles
and The Shoes were ready
for me to walk into the world.

The Primary stood like a judgement
on the north-face of a drumlin.

All summer, I climbed that hill
with The Shoes like fireworks
on the ends of my legs.
Dashing against the road-metal,
I loved those flintlock segs.
In the autumn, the sparks
they struck made bonfires.

Winters were vicious,
and the glacier spread itself
down from the summit of the street,
engulfing camber, gutter, kerb and causey.
And The Shoes betrayed me.
Their power was gone.
They walked on water once
but never took to ice.
Every morning I crawled on dunted knees
with the crampons of my finger-nails
hauling me up the hill.
Four o'clock was an ignominy
of clowning and skittering
downhill all the way
to the stanchion of the bus-stop
and an accolade of sneers.

I could stand no longer.
The shoes of a lifetime
were sneaked into a cupboard,
supplanted by a pair
of sandals with buckles
and rubber soles and holes
that let the slush in.

Finally, The Shoes were unearthed
in the base of the wardrobe,
treeless, their tongues hanging out,
splitting like old wood. They lay
bearded with dust, beside a string-bag
of my pa-pa's ancient bowls,
a set of coriaceous globes,
smug from a lifetime's use.

By then I had a pair
of Chelsea-boots that would never stop
when anyone they happened to know
lost their footing.

Aonghas MacBhàtair

SEAR AIR EDEN

Tha mo chadal mì-shochrach na h-oidhcheannan seo, agus mo bhruadaran buaireasach. Bidh mi a' bruadar san oidhche agus a' cuimhneachadh air beatha eile a bh' againn, ma dh'fhaoite, o chionn fhada an t-saoghail.

Bha sinn ann an gàrradh, ise 's mi-fhìn. Ann an gàrradh cho farsainn 's nach faiceadh sinn na bha air an taobh thall – ma 'se rud e 's gun robh muir no tìr air an taobh thall idir. Bha sinn a' tighinn heò air measan nan craobhan agus air na lusan a bha a' fàs sa' ghàrradh. Ged a bha an gàrradh a' cur thairis le ainmhidhean de gach seòrsa cha do dh'ith sinn gin dhiubh. Cha robh alt againn air an glacadh, ged a bha iad gun amharus romhainn, agus leis an fhìrinn innse, cha tàinig am miann oirnn beothaichean itheadh. Cha tàinig an toiseach co-dhiù.

Bha na craobhan 's na speuran làn de dh'eòin. Eòin ioma-dhathte a bhiodh ri caithream gun sgur. Cha robh na h-eòin ann ris an canar an t-seabhag, 's am fitheach, 's a' chom-hachag, 's an fhang, oir cha robh marbhadh anns a' ghàrradh agus cha robh bàs.

Bha an t-àile blàth sa' ghàrradh agus do bhrìgh sin cha do dh'aithnich sinn fuachd. Cha robh sinn ag ionndrainn teine. Cha robh fios againn fiù's dè an rud a bha ann an teine.

'Na mo bhruadaran bidh mi a' faicinn gach rud mar gum biodh on taobh a-muigh. Ach aig an aon àm is orm fhìn a bhios mi a' coimhead. Bidh mi a' mothachadh do bhòidhchead na mnà a bha sa' ghàrradh cuide rium. Bidh mi a' moladh a fuilt fada rèidh, a cìochan làna, a broinn mhìn. Tha i cho òg anns a' bhruadar. Tha mi air dìochuimhneacheadh gun robh i cho òg a-riamh.

Anns a' ghàrradh fhèin cha tug mi an aire flù's gun robh sinn nochdte. Bha sinn mar phiuthair is bràthair. Bha sinn mar chloinn... Cha robh. Bha sinn na bu neochiontaiche na sin, ma 'se 'neochiontach' am facal ceart.

Chuireadh sinn seachad an ùine a' coiseachd romhainn,

ann an caochladh cheàrnan den ghàrradh. Bhlasadh sinn de dhifir measan is lusan an siud 's an seo, agus uime sin cha do dh'aithnich sinn acras no sàth. Bha cùbhraidheached eadar-dhealaichte air gach meas is lus, is a h-uile fear dhiubh milis no blasmhor. Cha do dh'aithnich sinn searbhachd.

Bha na làithean fada grianach. Cha robh eòlas againn air dìle no sneachd no reothadh. Roimh glasadh an là dh'èireadh driùchd às an talamh, ag uisgeachadh freumhan nan craobhan 's nan lusan agus a' lìonadh nan sruthan. Cha do dh'fhuiling sinn pathadh.

Ged a bha cainnt againn cha tric a bhruidhneadh sinn. Cha robh sinn air a bhith beò ann an àite sam bith ach a-mhàin sa' ghàrradh. Cha robh mòmaid ann nach robh sinn còmhla. Cha robh fios no eòlas agam nach robh aice-se. Dè fon ghrèin a bhiodh sinn air cur an cèill? Cho fad 's a bha fios againn – agus ma 'se rud e 's gun do smaointich sinn air sin a-riamh – cha robh duine beò air uachdar na talmhainn ach a-mhàin sinn-fhèin. Cò ris a bhiodh sinn air bruidhinn?

Ma 'se an fhìrinn a th' aig na feallsanaich – gur e caochladh a th' ann an tìm – cha do dh'aithnich sinn tìm anns a' ghàrradh na bu mhotha. Ged a bha latha agus oidhche ann, bha na làithean 's na h-oidhcheannan coltach ris na làithean 's na h-oidhcheannan a chaidh romhpa agus a thàinig as an dèidh. Ged a bha ceàrnan a' ghàrraidh eadar-dhealaichte on a chèile, bhiodh an ceàrn ùr a lorgadh sinn gach là coltach ris na ceàrnan eile ann am bith coileanta.

Ach tìm ann no às, is dòcha gun robh sinn ag atharrachadh beag air bheag, oir bidh bruadar eile a' tighinn thugam bho àm gu àm.

Bha sinn ann an ceàrn den ghàrradh far an robh rèidhlean ann, agus ann an ceart mheadhan an rèidhlein bha craobh mhòr a' fàs. Laigh sinn air ar druim fo dhubhair na craoibhe, anns an fheur bhlàth, agus sheall sinn suas gu measan na craoibhe a bha sughmhor dearg am measg nan geugan. Chunnaic sinn gluasad dubh a' gliosrachadh air stoc na craoibhe agus thèirig nathair às an duilleach. Shuain e e-fhèin mu shliasaid Eubha, shnaig e thar a broinne mìne is eadar a cìochan làna, dh'èirich e a cheann gus an robh a bheul a' suathadh ri a beul-se, agus bhruidhinn e.

"Coimhead ort fhèin ann an sgàthan mo shùil. Tha thu

bòidheach a bhean, ach chan eil fios agad dè a th' ann am bòidhchead. Tha inntinn agad ach chan eil fios agad fiù's dè a th' ann an reusanachadh. Tha faireachdainnean annad nach deachaidh an dùsgadh. Tha cumhachd annad nach deachaidh a fuasgladh. Tha thu a' caitheamh do làithean anns a' ghàrradh seo gun tuigse air na nìthean a th' agad 's gun fios air na nìthean nach eil."

Chuir briathran na nathrach bruaillean 'nar n-aigne – fair-reachdainn ùr, ach nach robh gu buileach mì-thaitneach dhuinn. Bhon àm sin is ann le sùil ùr a chunnaic sinn an gàrradh, agus bhiodh sinn a' ceasnachadh a' chèile gun sgur. "An saoil am bheil àite eile ann ach a-mhàin an gàrradh?" "An saoil am b'urrainn dhuinn biadh eile itheadh ach a-mhàin measan is lusan?" "An saoil am bi daoine eile ann anns an àm ri teachd?" "An saoil am bi sinn ann an sheo, anns a' ghàrradh, gu sìorraidh bràth?"

Agus ge b'e an ceàrn den ghàrradh anns a bhiodh sinn feadh an latha, lorgadh sinn gach feasgar slighe an rèidhlein, gus eisdeachd ri briathran meallach na nathrach.

Air an latha deireannach, an uair a thèirig an nathair à geugan na craoibhe, bha meas sughmhor dearg 'na bheul. Shìn e gu Eubha e agus thug i grèim air. Ged is mi-fhìn a thug ainm do gach nì a bh' anns a' ghàrradh, cha robh ainm agam air a' mheas àlainn sin. Shuain an nathair e-fhèin mu shliasaid Eubha, shnaig e thar a broinne mìne is eadar a cìochan làna, dh'èirich e a cheann gus an robh a bheul a suathadh ri a beul-se, agus bhruidhinn e.

"'S e seo ubhal craobh an eòlais" ars an nathair. "Ma dh'itheas sibh dheth, thig sibh beò ann an da-rìribh. Aithnichidh sibh acras is fuachd, pian is teas, sgìos is ionndrainn is bròn. Aithnichidh sibh gal is gàire, gaol is fuath, caoibhneas is eud". Thionndaidh Eubha do m'ionnsaigh. "An dh'ith sinn dheth?"

"Ithidh."

Is ann mar sin a thig mo bhruadar gu crìoch. Chan urrainn dhomh gun a bhith a' smaointeachadh air – an uair a bhios mi ag obair anns a' ghàrradh a chruthaich mi às a ghainmhich, le fallas dubh mo bhodhaige; an uair a bhios mi còmhla ri mo chuid-mhac, is sinn ri òl, 's ri seinn, 's ri sabaid; an uair a bhios mi 'nam laighe còmhla ri mo bhean ann an dorchadas na h-oidhche, no a' faicinn, ann an solas ùr na maidne, nam preasan a tha mun cuairt air a sùilean is i 'na cadal.

Uaireannan bidh mi a' smaointeachadh gum bu toigh leam gàrradh mo bhruadair a lorg, aig a' cheann thall. Ach fada nas trice na sin bidh mi ag iarraidh a bhith cùidhteas mo bhruadaran meallach. Bidh mi a' saoilsinn gum b' fheàrr leam gu mòr fuireachd ann an sheo, fo stoirmean eagalach, fo chamhanaich iongantach an fhàsaich.

Peter McCarey

STRANGERS IN THE NIGHT

1

Two pieces of advice. Don't lend money to the secretaries. They know you're earning a lot more than them though they don't know how much. Tell them your hotel's expensive. It's true. And, it's up to you, if you want to then go ahead it's about 15000 CFA a night. I had a good run for my money till about ten years ago, but they did a random check on some prostitutes in town two years ago and seven out of ten were seropositive. They're stuck for clients so they're very persistent. Tell them your wife's arriving. Reading? That's a good idea. What have you brought? Trocchi? How did you come across him? He was a great friend of mine. We were working together at the time he wrote *Cain's Book*. Yes, I know he's dead. Took heroin for years. Said he'd live till he was seventy. Fifty-nine wasn't too far off. He had two kids. Beautiful wife. He brought her to Paris to sleep on the floor of a chambre de bonne. Deserted her after four years and took up with an Amerindian girl. Then she left him for a photographer. Then something about a publisher who married money. You know what happened? The money went to a partouze. A what? A partouse. What's that? It's where everybody's on the floor fucking everybody else. And when she saw – he held his hands apart at chin level, if he was going to tell me he'd caught a trout that size I wasn't going to believe him – the size of the instrument that whatsisname produced in her honour, her there on the carpet, she decided to get married to him! Pat was cackling red in the face. His eyes disappeared, all you could see was the liverish bits under the lids.

2

Excision? Female circumcision. To devotees of a certain world religion the woman is such a base creature that she should have no enjoyment. She does not reach orgasm, which prolongs the pleasure for the man. No, infibulation is removal of the clitoris. Then some of them stitch up the vagina until marriage, then sometimes make a slip with the knife and the woman is ruined. Meanwhile in parts of the Congo, mothers tease out the labia of their daughters, so that when they grow they sort of flap around. So they become excited and are suffused with blood. The penis is enveloped in a conch – my colleague tells me. For me, it is time to go home. I have an African wife, she does not speak French, but I have promised her a ticket home every few months, there are some cheap flights. I asked for a transfer – to Rwanda, it is beautiful there, there are the lakes, there are gorillas in the highlands. That American woman who studied them, she was murdered, some say by poachers, some say her boyfriend wanted to use her notes. That one who was here, she drank, she took drugs, and her boyfriend, they said they saw him beating her up. She was very nice most of the time, but she got very low, and when she thought she could get no lower... I've been here fourteen years. I've made an official complaint that they wouldn't let me have my transfer – look at all this correspondence – but someone from head office has told me confidentially that I am going to lose. I've a few months left, I file my reports quickly then I go where I like.

3

It's raining. In an hour it will be hot again... No, I'm from Ghana. There in the dry season it's hot and in the rainy season it rains. Now it will be hot. I was there for nearly two months, December and January. My children are at school there. And my wife is there. I wanted to send them to school here but there is no English school, no international school, and the French school – here if you do not know the boss you get nowhere. If you are intelligent it doesn't matter. The minister's son gets his exams because his father says I am the minister. They should let intelligent people move ahead if they want the country to move, but here everyone stays down and expects the government to do everything for them. My father could not read, my mother could not read, we were from a small village. My grandfather... There is no competition here. In Nigeria, in Ghana, people are always moving. Here there was a white man living in one of those houses there. The yard was full of rubbish, he said who planted that corn? There were corn cobs big as my forearm growing. They said nobody: there must have been corn dropped there with the rest and he said you're blessed here. You don't know that in Europe to grow maize at all you have to care for it and you never get cobs as big as that. There's a Ghanaian nearby. He planted yams. Now he's got yams growing big as my thigh. They're blessed here, but they don't know it. I've been working here ten years. My children are ten, eight and six. Two girls and a boy. My wife will maybe come here in April.

4

The match is being played in Algeria. Cameroon's winning, but they're a good team. Did you hear about the game last night? The Somalis and the Egyptians were knocking hell out of each other, breaking up the benches. And according to the world service the Yugoslavs and the Romanians were doing the same thing. Where are you from? Scotland? I've got Irish blood. On my mother's side. No, she's not Congolese, her people were from Togo, Ghana, and some Irish – my great grandfather was Irish. My father was Breton. Not really Breton – Chouan. But all this stuff in British football, then Northern Ireland. Chauvinism.

The Batéké. They're everywhere. Not just in the Batéké plateau, but up river, on *both* sides, down the south road, over into Zaire. You know there are eternal snows in Zaire? Everything grows there, oranges, grapes. There are people there with eyes the colour of yours; very tall, and black – like the Ethiopians, say, but with blue eyes. They call them the lion men. Because of the eyes.

Before I bought the restaurant I owned 17 barges. 800 m^3, 2600 horsepower engines. We'd go up the tributaries of the Congo to load – 380 km to the Lima – the only tributary in the world that's navigable all year round. 30 m deep in places. A strange mixture of savannah and rainforest growing there. No buoys: we just always kept to the treegrown side. It goes more than 900 km, up to Cameroon. There we'd load up. Auban. See that table there? That's made of auban. It's the only wood that sinks in water. Ebony? It floats or sort of sinks, don't know, but auban – barges loaded with it have capsized. Years later they've hauled up the trunks, and the water hadn't begun to penetrate. The termites break their teeth on that stuff. I have a photo of myself beside an auban log 3.5 m in diameter. The archway over there is less than 3 m.

We'd bring it back down the Congo. I love that river! They've sounded it at over 300 m deep (a thousand feet!) among the hills. At Sandy Beach it's 52 km wide. Pilots from the Netherlands are working on it constantly, charting the sandbanks and shifting the buoys.

What do people do between here and Kinshasa? Traffic. What do you mean? Traffic. Well, a tin of sardines costs less here than in Kinshasa. Paper for newspapers costs less there. Traffic. Well (whispers) engines. They cost much less in Kinshasa. I took over a barge for 250 tons of sand. I had two boats run alongside in port there. I said one had broken down. I got the engine changed, and sold the old one; brought the new one back and sold it here. Then a Greek in Kinshasa wanted to sell a tug and barge. A big one. I was interested. I got a Zairian crew. I paid them well. I bought the boat. We went upstream. Quite a long way. We ran down the Zairian flag, and we ran up the Congolese flag. We repainted the funnel with our insignia. Now, ships have serial numbers. We chiselled them off and welded on new ones then we did it up with sulphuric acid, to age it a bit. The thing to remember is, when you have to get past government officials, wait till there's an election on or something that fills their mind with politics: that way they just want you out of the way, fast. We sold the tug and barge to the Congolese government.

5

One is serial, one is parallel. The hotel is parallel and the continent serial. I mean, not only are hotels all the same, they're meant to be – chains of Hilton, Pullman, Novo – or other hotels so you know what to expect. In a way it helps, like knowing you can get washed and fed as usual, and in another way it couldn't be more alienating: you suddenly look round the room and for a moment you don't recall what country you're in. Like airports it makes for amnesia, not the neurological variety, but the communal one. The hotel has parallels everywhere but no serial: each day is like the previous one, whose traces are erased – more carefully in the more expensive places – day by day. One therefore tries to enter the world of serial time, carefully, so one can get back out when one wants. (One? I *never* say one. What's the game?) Because I don't want to stay in Africa. I want back home to my family.

Trouble is – how do you introduce yourself to such a foreign place? I looked out the hotel restaurant window last night at the river, and the lights of Kin, where I can't go. I couldn't even go outside because I'd left the insect repellent in my room; in fact, to get to my room I had to run the gamut of hures in the lobby. You can become African, as Pat largely has, but that means letting Africa feed you – no imported camembert and Evian; it means opening yourself up to Africa's life, swimming in her rivers, probably entertaining the viruses and parasites from time to time, letting her into your room at night I won't become African. Still, today I went out of town with friends, whose daughter had never been out of Brazza before, or seen anyone so white as me. We bought food from roadside stalls and breezeblock barbecues – fish, pili-pili and onions smoked in manioc leaves, and we ate it in a village hut formerly used for party meetings. Long live perestroika. Hope my stomach holds out.

6

After six days eating in the hotel restaurant I could stand it no longer. They only have one cassette of muzack, and they play it morning and night: Downtown, Strangers in the Night, Yesterday, and the food was just as good. So on a passing consultant's recommendation I went to the Beach restaurant, 200 yards from the hotel, right on the water's edge, beside the ramp for the Kinshasa ferry. During the day that bit of road is crowded with people, women with babies on their backs and bundles on their heads, cripples in hand-pedalled trikes being pushed by boys with twin cataracts, through the biggest concentration of pickpockets in Brazza. This evening there was no one there, though because of the powercut I would only have seen a white face anyway. I made my way down the middle of the road to the fingernail gleam of the restaurant. Two middle-aged women at a table just inside the door greeted me, and I muttered something back. People don't usually say hello to me here, and it was only when I got past them I realised they were white. There were big tarpaulins down over the shore side of the restaurant, which had a low balustrade and a rail, but no glass windows. A steady breeze was pushing the tarpaulins, so they breathed in on the restaurant like the flank of a huge eel. The waitress lit a candle for me to read the menu by. There was a vast and quiet rhythm from the other side of the sheets, and the hiss of calor gas lamps among the candles. It was only now that I connected the mannerist lighting with the powercut. Three other men arrived one after the other, and we were disposed at different corners of the long room, none facing any other. Are men all terrified of each other? The lady acts as though we were. The rhythm from the Congo was the very distant engine of a small boat. Fronds and shoots of potted tropical plants, yellowy green in the candle light, livid in the gas, one ceiling tile unpeeling; I ordered capitaine à la provençale, which they did over a fire. The phone rang a couple of times. It was on a wooden desk on a dais at the bottom of the room, beside a gas lamp that a vase of dried flowers was bending close to. I couldn't read, which is my usual technique for becoming invisible in restaurants, so I shielded the candle and tried to hear what the river was thinking. It's sad without music, said the proprietrix. I realised how lucky I was. 'Je suis laide' she said during one of her chats on the phone. I didn't have to look up. The waitress, whose name was Florence, was pretty, with an Al Jolson voice. She wore a yellow frock with white spots, an apron top with just straps at the back, her hair was in a bun, and she had a solemn, childish expression. She clumped round on her heels as the owner told her to do this, Florence do that, thinking I may be ugly, but I do have some style. The owner came and removed the other crockery – unless you are expecting une compagne? A pity, she said. So it was. The tarpaulins were limp, now, behind the long frieze with a tropical riverside painted on it, so they opened one, and the river was so wide that the light from the arc lamps at Kin harbour hardly made it across the stream. Next evening I went to the same place. They had the electricity back, and piped muzack that spoiled the heavy breathing of the Congo.

7

At the end of a two-and-a-half hour mass in St Anne's cathedral we got a half-hour appeal for 200 tons of cement, plus sand, plus gravel, to build a bell tower, to compete with the other churches in town. Who needs it? But the agnus dei: that was something. It got off to an atrocious start, the trebles completely out of tune with the electric organ, but then the rest of the choir kicked in and called the tune, and the organ played along. Glorious. My guitar teacher, who had spent some years in Uganda, once explained to me that the natural octave is the difference between the open string and the twelfth fret. The well-tempered, European octave is the difference between the open string and the twelfth fret harmonic. This was twenty years ago, so I may have mixed things up, but anyway he said the slightly wider, natural octave is what gives African music its peculiar brightness. Now the electric organ in the choirloft was probably Japanese, tuned in the European way. You could hear it piping up from time to time just slightly wrong, but the African song was big enough to bear it. I hope they're as tolerant of us when their time comes. That way of singing reminds me, once in Leningrad on the umpteenth fiddler's bidding to go and sing Scottish songs, I ungraciously left my guitar at home. That didn't get me off, so I ended up singing unaccompanied, tapping the table for the bodhran beat. Polite applause. They asked the young lad sitting next to me to sing. He paused, breathed in through his nose, and sang an orthodox hymn in a voice that shook the windows and brought tears to my eyes. It was so breathtaking I didn't even feel foolish in comparison. At the end he apologised: he had sung sitting down, so he hadn't been able to give the hymn the full treatment. Turns out he was rated number two in the city, much in demand on religious feast days.

8

I dined a couple of times last week with Venkatesh Mannar, a Hindu from Madras, speaker of a Dravidian language close to Tamil. He can pick his way through the scriptures in Sanskrit, but reads English for relaxation – though he prefers speaking his own language in Madras. He enjoyed Peter Brook's film of the Mahabharata, but then he enjoyed Attenborough's Ghandi too. He owns a factory that produces iodised salt and tours Africa and Asia three or four months in the year for international organisations (for money really, he says) advising on the industrial process, a fairly simple matter of spraying salt with an iodine compound.

Iodine deficiency results in hypothyroidism, goitre and in severe cases, cretinism. The severe cases tend to be found in isolated mountain communities far from the sea, where iodine has been leached from the soil in the process of erosion.

On Saturday evening I had just gone through the worst day in a week of the flux and I was kind of sorry for myself, and glad to join Venkatesh and a colleague of his – never mind the name. Early 50s, thick specs and a Captain Ahab beard. Laughs a lot, but watches you while laughing. He was being one of the lads, but when Venkatesh informed me at one point that the Professor was a world expert on iodine deficiency, he gravely let the accolade sink in: just so's you know I'm a world expert, boys. All the same, he was a brave man: when he was stationed on the Zairian border with Rwanda and he had a boat to commute to the island where he worked, he spent two nights once ferrying 120 people across the lake and out of an area where each of 60 mercenaries led a squad of kids who were armed and constantly high on hemp.

Twenty-five years ago, when he was twenty-six, he went to work on Kivou Lake, in eastern Zaire. The lake is 1400 m up – the height of Ben Nevis, and the island, which is 50 km long and 15 wide, rises to 2500 m above sea level. In the mornings early it was beautiful, mist rising from the water, from the tops of the high forest. His wife stayed on shore with the children and he worked on the island, staying there Monday to Friday, with an 'old nurse' of about 40: old to a young man. They had two houses to stay in. One was palatial, at the north end, with water on two sides, and a vast dining table for the two of them. They worked hard and hectic, vaccinating children by the thousand. He worked there for two-and-a-half years.

The conversation moved on to later missions here and there, degenerating into airport delays and awful hotels, then that anecdote about the rescue operation, but he returned quite often to Kivou Lake, the touchstone of his life, with a kind of reverence. You hear many an aid official talking about The Field with a kind of reverence – the early experience (or reported experience) that gives sense to their programmes, their development and their implementation. Does it? Is it reverence or sentimentality? Two years ago he returned to Kivou Lake. Twenty-five years back it had a population of 30,000 and the mountain forest was a national park. Now it had a population of 80,000 and the forest was gone.

The island is the world. We vaccinate everyone, and they don't die of smallpox or TB, or yellow fever or whooping cough or plague. That's wonderful. We distribute iodine in oil or salt or water – and goitre disappears, and the shocking cases of cretinism. We grow up healthy and cut down the trees. We fish in dugout canoes with outboard motors. The sappy branches crackle under the cookpots and grills. The fish are fattening on human waste in the freshets. The rain flushes the topsoil into the lake. It flushes the iodine into the lake.

9

I stopped writing to go across to the Central café for a brochette and was lucky enough to bump into people I knew: Neil Joseph and his wife Marika. I had just finished the food and my first bottle of beer in over a week when this tall thin fellow came round the corner with a cardinal's cap and two feathers sticking up, carrying a tomtom, his face painted. He was followed by a smaller variant without a cap, and a third who was carrying a rough xylophone about a yard wide. Four dancing girls lined up behind them. Another tall thin man, in civilian clothes, announced the regular Saturday evening entertainment, a dance troupe, and suggested that we all drink 'Primus, la bière du pays'. Marika whispered something to Joseph. Oh yes, he said, two of the dancers are whores from the local nightclub. I spotted one of them easily: she couldn't dance, and her tongue and her tummy hung out as she stared at all the men while going through her lewd motions. The musicians set up a rhythm, and the dancers shuffled about behind them. I thought this was an odd configuration, but presently each of the four came out to do a quick turn. The first was kind of squat and flat, with a pretty face. She held her head very high and smiled into space. She moved well, switching smoothly from one position to another. Next was the bovious I'm sorry the obvious whore, and the next was the one Joseph found youngest and prettiest. She could dance too, but she had this way of squinting into space that I associate with people who are led along the pavement by golden labradors. They all came on together to dance, and it was then I realised that they weren't improvising – unless the fourth dancer, who led them, was improvising and they were watching closely. Each wore a piece of yellow cloth around the hips, and another around the bust, tied at the back in a big knot. White paint was daubed from neck to navel and down the thighs, the shins and calves, then across the forehead, nose and cheekbones. Number four had a diamond stud in one nostril and chewed gum throughout the performance. She was a marvellous dancer. For the second formal dance they took up poles and came out nimbly from behind the musicians as though rowing a pirogue (which is propelled like a gondola or punt). They knelt down and carried on with the dance, flapping their elbows and flailing their heads, then they started to caress the poles in a way that suggested they weren't meant to be oars anymore. Marika laughed as Joseph and I registered the change. In another dance one did the splits, but it looked all wrong, a foreign intrusion, and she got up awkwardly so as not to skin her thighs on the pavement. There was a certain attitude all the dances shared, especially as performed by the squat girl and the slim one with the diamond: the pelvis rolls like the deck of a ship in high seas. The bare feet go down heel first and seem to clasp the ground, insisting on the earth. Feet and knees are turned outwards, shoulderblades are pushed tight together and the back is arched, so the breast and the mons are offered to the audience. It was all too much for me, there in the front line. I kept taking refuge in my glass and conversation about the British Empire. The dance was highly erotic – and equally beautiful, and that was what surprised me. Classical ballet, to me, is beautiful but hardly erotic, the way it's always taking off for the sublime. Erotic performances in Europe take place in a kind of sexual cliché (or Clichy) and there's always something grim, or sad, or frivolous about them. These African dances are about sex, and they say that sex is what it's about. Life is short, death is everywhere, this dancer is woman and woman is good. The slim one was completely in control, and seemed rather detached, maybe because she was chewing gum. She hardly glanced at the audience to check our reaction, but she quite often looked at herself: she'd watch a hand as it gestured, or consider her navel as it went its way, and these quizzical, hawklike movements of her head and neck were further gestures in the dance. I caught sight of an old barman indoors in his white shirt and bowtie sending them up, grinning from ear to ear. Joseph's favourite danced over with the collection plate. As she stopped at the next table Joseph said 'dites: après, vous invitez mon ami à danser?' Her back was to us, there was a trickle of sweat between her shoulderblades, her hips were still grinding but the plate she held out was steady. 'Oui.' She spoke French! What a disappointment. A few minutes later the squat one danced over and tried to yank me to my feet. She could have had a career in sumo wrestling. I declined, I refused, I extricated my hand from hers. Me, the cripple of the discothèque, the spanner in the ceilidh. Anyhow, I had a suitcase to pack.

Derrick McClure

THE ARK O THE COVENANT

(Owerset frae the Gàidhlig o Ruaraidh MacThòmais)

1. Houbeit we Gaed Different Gates

Houbeit we gaed different gates,
houbeit the crosses our shiels bure warna as ane,
houbeit my lips war blaspheimious,
ye wid aiblins unnerstaun whit it wes.
Houbeit I widna say it
fearin tae pyne ye,
an ye widna speir it
fearin I wid lee tae ye,
a ken-na-whit wes there
haudin our howp tae its course,
houbeit ye war ettlin for siccarness
an nae howp for me cud siccarness hecht.
Houbeit there wes winter an simmer,
lown an bowder,
dout, speirin, repone,
houbeit a gullion wes there
the grùnn wes even.
Houbeit daith wes there
daith hent us nane in his cleik.

2. When ye Apent yon Buik

When ye apent yon buik
ye kent that a truith wid come tae ye,
that your finger wid ligg on a portion;
there wes strinth in your trouin.
I fann yon strinth
in the lowp o my bluid,
the flourish o't
on the pores o my huil,
tho my finger cud ne'er be sae siccar.

3. The Questioner

'Hae ye howp,'
the gentie bodie says tae me,
'we twa will be thegither
in eternitie?'
A cauld question in the middle o simmer.
It wes closer tae himsel,
an he wes greinin for't;
for him yon place
wes lik a hame he hedna kent
frae youthheid's oncome,
warm in memory's waps,
siccar in fancy's bosie,
but gleg as the lift o spring.
He wes walkin awa til't
ower a broun muir,
ower a tuim waste
wi the heicht o the bens abuin,
an ayont the horizon
wes a waal, an an ingle.
He wes wantin
his freins tae finn the wey,
an tae win til't as pleasit them best:
he widna gar them hirsel,
there nae howpin nor hirslin in eternitie.

4. Donald Roddy

When ye begoud wi the psaum
we war borne awa
on yon slouthy spatrils
tae anither airt,
hauf-gaits atween Canaan an Garrabost,
wi ferliefu trees growin frae the peat,
crowdie an orangers on the buird,
names an airts frae hyne awa,
fremmit fowk in plaid an mutch,
Ruth an Naomi at the fit o the croft,
Joseph that gaed doun on the *Iolaire*.

5. The Haa

The kennin o years ye hed
o yon haa;
whitna graithin wes in it,
whaur the columns war
an hou they war shapit,
an the Keing's throne;
an aft did ye hae your crack
wi the Ane that sat on it;
ye kent Him as weel
as gin He bade in Bernera.
I never heard whit boat
wes gaun tae cairry ye ower
but it wid wheech ye ower in jist a gliff.

6. Life Ayebidin

For aye wid it bide,
yon life.
Nae five-nichts' fivver wid come ower't
nor hidlin teesic.
It widna get pat tae the grunn wi the jows,
nor flung on the midden frae the factor;
it wes safe frae the straik o a bagnet,
the weed widna tak it awa.
Hinnie-sweet it wid be,
wi butter an fish
an hertsome cracks,
hymns an psaums,
chaumer-daffin
an brose in the mornin.

7. Fishermen

Fishermen they war theirsels,
forbye.
The sea wes mair gowstier,
the auncient craigs mair grumlier,
mauger the glents o the sun;
but furth they gaed wi the same mangin,
an the same hunger,
an the fowk they telt their news til
wes jist as near the yird,
an kent the stanes as weel –
for ballast onygaits –
an unnerstuid the pouer
o Ane wha cud turn them intil laifs,
or rowe a muckle ane awa frae the mou o His graff.

8. Sea Wirship

Gaun ower in the boat tae the kirk,
daurk suits an white sarks an reid faces,
muckle neives an willin oars,
cense o spindrift, cense o prayer,
mellin as ane,
wirship frae hythe tae hyne.

9. Takin the Buiks

Doun on our knees,
our elbucks on the bink,
the forenuin wi its wee eternitie,
the lowsit dug
stravaigin doun the road –
Oh for a cairt!
The nock strikin ten,
my granda proggin words
intae the rammy;
a laverock
crackin wi the Creator;
an oar gettin haikit on buird,
thole-pins gaun craik in the Hope.
'Ye hear ilka word we say tae Ye
in the lown o Your halie mornin.'
Whitna frichtsome bizz frae the eggies sotterin in the pan!

10. Bonnieheid Banned

Dowie it wes, that bonnieheid wes banned:
the waas war straucht an bare,
the winnocks war fower-neukit,
the distemper hed nae warmin intil't,
ye cudna gae doun on your knees in the kirk
wiout sinnin,
sattlin in the want o stuils,
the lichts war white an cauld:
but ae cross there wes,
on a gair o sulk in the poupit;
we warna aa an haill redd o the Ruid.

Bonnieheid smuirit,
hair hauden ticht wi preens,
flagaries flemit awa,
aathing winnin tae daurk
an drumlieheid.
But a waff o a smirkle wid daw,
dwaiblie as distemper,
at the heid o the dais
at skailin-time,
a gruppin o hauns in the porch,
an auntrin snirt outby.
In the caur
ye cud hae a richt lauch –
jist douce-like.

But for aa yon
the kirk wes like an eedol,
houbeit there wes nae skellie een tae't;
streekit, cauld,
ne'er a thraw,
ill tae touch,
nae scog o turnin,
a cauld ee in its foreheid,
on your rig as ye smoolit awa frae its goamin,
marble tae kiss,
a hert o stane intil't.

An auntrin body there wes
gaed in wi their bonnieheid an cam out wi't
no smuirit.

11. An Intimation o Thaem that's Awa
(First Sawbath o Janwar 1979)

Iain, Ewan's Calum's lad, frae Flesherin,
on sic a like day.
Himsel an his wife aye loed ither weel,
a muckle faimily they hed, wi oes forby,
a hous fu an skailin ower,
hertsome in their natur,
bruikin a fouth o walth,
takin the Buik morn an een:
a tuim howe in their hame the nicht.

Calum, Finlay's Murdo's lad, frae Bayble,
on so me ither day:
aye blythe tae be bousin he wes in his youthheid,
an blythe tae be winchin,
or the teesic cam ower him;
his mither an sister's still tae the fore,
there some fowk says
it wes thaem that brocht him ben
at the last Sacrament.
He wesna lang ben.

Neil, Norman's Sandy's lad, frae Garrabost,
on Ne'erday:
a merchant,
he hainit meal in the First War
till the price gaed up –
it wesna foustie aa an haill.
His bacca wes dear,
an he reekit like a lum.
In ill dreams he wid see caumels,
gousty scaups wi ne'er a rug tae finn.

Mairi, Muckle Hector's lass, frae Knock,
a week past the nicht:
the lad that wes gaun tae mairry her
wes tint in France
at the hint o December
1917.

12. Reid Jock's Prayer

There's Yoursel
sittin on Your throne,
no a thing can pass ye by.
Whit wey, then, hae ye latten us
stravaig sae faur abreid?
Whit wey did ye thole sae muckle
when we war herkenin the dunt o the pulse,
when the sellie said til's,
'Tak, dinna deny,'
when pride gart our inwittins crine?
Whit wey did ye lea the blinners on Your Kirk
in the heicht o nune,
an smuir the caunle
when we war seekin Your altar?
Oursels that's fankl't in Your net,
spare-na us Your knife.

13. Whipper-In

A gawsie heid wi a hassock o hair
in the elders' foredais,
a lion o langsyne,
a Canmore in his youthheid;
when we stuid up for the prayer
he wid face the congregaution,
great een faain on ilka row,
a cross confrontin ilka bodie there:
a whipper-in he wes, on Sawbath days an ouk-days,
but unco, unco bousome tae the Maister.

14. Judgement or Chance

The deid-kist's wecht on the buird,
on the airm
that ye dusht him out the boat wi
in the middle o the War,
passin judgement.
Frae the Judge he gat anither chance,
an frae yoursel.
His judgement, is't, come ower him nou,
or his chance?

15. At the Question

When ye stuid up for the Question
the lang daises eeliet out o sicht,
a scog cam ower the Sawbath blaiks,
nae scanse ye saw o mutch or bunnet,
the poupit dern't awa,
an een the Buik's ain sel wes pitten by,
an ye war back in yon bar
at the English fishin
whaur ye cam face tae face
wi the Creator.
Wha wid tyne siccan a memorie?

16. Glesca wes your Egypt

Glesca wes your Egypt,
an a hantle o ye gaed there in your youthheid
when hunger cam ower your hames:
doun ye gaed amang the fremmit gods,
in the steirin o the streets
ye herkent the leids o the gentiles
an gat pack wi them,
ye blethered wi the temple huirs
in Hope Street,
and happ't your bouks in Lawlan claes
on Setterday efternunes,
ye drank your drauchts o their wine
an cam tae bruik the gust o their breid.
But your Faither caad ye back tae your ain kintra
for his fowk tae growe fouthie in the Promised Lann.

17. Prayer

My prayer
is ne'er tae be funn
in my need, on my knees,
ae day or ony
at prayer.

Ronald W. McDonald

THE ROTTANS' FLITTIN

Fairmers afore i war aye said they wis ae step fae the peers-hoose an Peter Mitchell haed an afa chauve tae mak a livin at Blackmyres. He'd jist ma fadder as ploomin an the orra loon tae keep the place ga'in an it wis gey sair wirk on Blackmyres steeny parks.

The cottar hoose backit the midden an wis jist a rickle o steens wi muckle holes i the door an oothouse. Bit it wis wirk or wint in thae days an naebody wis ony the waur for't.

Fadder's sairest trauchle wis keepin his pair o horse in maet. He haed tae mak dee an men the theats wi bits o binder twine an wire for ye haed mair chunce o finnin oot the Horseman's Wird fae a ploomin than gettin siller oot o Peter Mitchell. Ivry penny wis a prisoner an ivry fardin hoordet like gowd.

The steadin an fairm-hoose wis faain apairt an the place wis ill wi rottans. They wis aye scurrin an rummlin aroon the barn an the byre an awye wis fylit wi their dirt. Thir een wis teetin at ye fae ivry neuk an ye caud spy'm nippin ower the cupples o the stable. They haed a gran hidey-hole doon inside th'aul water-mull an nae trap or pizen seem't tae faze them ava. Hooiver, fan een wis foun in the bairn's pram, Peter wis obleeged tae caa in the ratcatcher, tho nae wi afa guid grace.

It wis twa days afore Andra cam blatterin up the fairm track oan is belaggeret aul motor-bike an side-car. Faur the side-car shud hae bin wis a muckle widden kist faur Andra cairted aa his gear. On tap sat es orra luikin beast caad Wullie fa micht hae bin a terrier. His lugs wis tattered like a tinkie's sark an his heid wis aa scrattet an scubbit wee fechtin rottans. The thocht o rottans made him loup doon an snuffel aroon the steadin wi's tail wuggin awa like the shaft o Tucker's engin.

Andra hissel luikit a proper bauchle: he'd lang, raggety hair croont wi a battered aul booler hat, moudieskin briks hud up wi galluses an a jaiket fair yirdit wi grease. But faan it came tae sortin oot rottans there wis naebody tae cap oor Andra.

Peter wis sweirt tae pairt wi Andra's usual chairge an the twa haed struck a bargain at haaf the ga'in rate. Andra noo baited up a wire cage an pit it i the barn.

In the mornin Peter cairtet't oot an stood it oan the neep cutter. A muckle broon rottan wis birslin away in ae corner. Us littleens were nae suppost tae be thair but we wirna gaen tae miss onythin an line't up on tap o the dyke tae see fit wis gaen on.

Richt on the meenit-heid Andra rattlit up in a clood o blue stinkin reek an pleitered throo the dubs o the fairm-yaird. He inspeckit the cage an gaed it a kick.

'At'll dae fine,' he declare't as the rottan birsed its teeth at'm.

'Fit are ee gaun tae dee with that naisty brute?' speert Peter.

'Jist ee watch es,' ses Andra an pullt oan a pair o muckle ledder gloves. He wis afa carefu tae open the door jist a wee bittie and slidit his haan in. He grippit the rottan ahin the neck an his thoom presst doon. The rottan jist lay there fair fushionless. Andra open't up a wee leather pyock and shoved the rottan's heid and top haaf in't an pull't the string ticht.

'At'll haud the bugger,' declare't Andra. He haaled aff the gloves and threeded up a big needle wi a puckle stoot black threed. We wis aa dumfoonered fan he startit tae shew up the rottan's erse. Fan he'd finished he jist flung it oan the midden an it skited away like lichtnin.

Peter wis fair bamboozlt. 'Help ma Boab, Andra, fit's aa that in aid o? Foos at ga'in tae clear oot the rottans?'

'Ye'll jist hae tae wyte an see, Peter,' he answert, packin up his gear an stowin't in ower i kist.

'Bit foo will ah ken if it wirks? Fit's ga'in tae happen?' Peter wis real worrit noo.

'Wyte or the morn,' said Andra, raikin his pooches fer a brookit aul cutty and a twist o bogie roll. He took is time stappin in a pucklie bacha an lichtin it wi a spunk. Eence it wis drawin fine he cairriet oan.

'Ye'll ken aa richt if its wirkin. Fit dae ye think wid happen tae yir intimmers if somebody shewed up yir erse?'

A puckle kicks wi the fit-stairt an aff he wint leavin Peter scrattin his heid.

That nicht er wis an afa thin reedy kinna skirl startit up an waakened Mrs Mitchell. Peter opent the winda luikin ower the steadin an glowert oot. Wi the caul win blawin up his sark he steed for a filie winnerin fit wis adee. Syne at last he oonersteed.

Lauchin awa tae hissel, he crawlt back in ower the bed an

snugglit doon unner i quilt.

'Stap yer lugs, Agnes,' he avised, 'Ye'll jist hae tae pit up wi't. Ah ken fit it is.'

In the wee sma oors o the mornin the young loon Phimister fae the oot-fairm at Burnt Top wis kneipen hame oan his bike. Wird wis he wis coortin the kitchie deem fae Smiddyhill. Onywey, is he chauved up this hill at Birken Braes he spied sic a frichtsome sicht that it stoppit him deid. There, richt in front o'im, wis a livin carpet ripplin ower the road.

It wis rottans: rottans by the thoosan; muckle eens an smaaer eens, aul eens an younger eens, weans carrit by thir mithers, aul eens wi'oot hair tow'd alang by younger fry; aa in ae muckle bourach. It feart the loon as sair at he couldna meeve; the hair o'is heid stood oan en. Haed his granfadder nae telt him o some gangrel body sleepin ahin a dyke being etten alive in a rottans' flitten?

Hooiver, the rottans passt im bye an he flew up the hill like the hemmers o hell. Blackmyers wisna fash't wi rottans fer a lang time, but Andra haed tae be caa'd in tae a puckle o the neebors fairms. An a reglar three hauf-croons wis nae tae be sneezt at in thae hard-up days.

Carl MacDougall

ZAK

Nobody's loved me like I love myself and nobody did what I did for myself.

I ran away when I was nine, got caught and came back, got caught and came back, again and again and again; I kept running till they got fed up bringing me back.

Ask them, ask anybody, ask them if they know me and they'll tell you; they'll tell you if they know me and I bet they know me cause they'll remember my name.

I changed my name when I ran away. They gave me a name I didn't want. Four other boys in the home had the same name. I don't need to tell you what it was, you know the kind of name, Thomas, Robert, John, William, James, names that are all right for some people, but not for me.

When I ran away I went to missions. They give you free food, sometimes clothes and a place to sleep. They hardly ever ask you questions. All you do is listen to a sermon, sing a few hymns and say you've been saved. Nobody ever told me what it meant being saved, nobody said what was supposed to happen, but if being saved meant the difference between soup, a sandwich, a cup of tea and fuck all, then I was saved. I got saved three times in the one fucken day, the same guy saved me four times and still doesn't know who I am.

They go on about strengthening your faith. I don't know what it means. They tell you not to be like Zacharias and read a bit from the Gospel According to Saint Luke, Chapter One, which goes on about John the Baptist's father who didn't have faith but he went to the temple where God struck him dumb and he got faith quick enough then all right. When they tell you that bit they say you shouldn't be like him, but they don't tell you if God sorted him out when he'd got the faith or not; they just say you shouldn't be like Zacharias and should strengthen your faith.

I liked his name and called myself after him.

My name is Zak.

My mammy never bothered and the oldman went away. Never knew him. I remember bits and pieces, presents and fights, police and the first time in a home. He came and cried and told us it was his fault and he'd make it up to us, he'd be back the next day to take us away back home where we'd have a party. That was the last time I saw him.

Somebody told me it would be better if I thought he was dead. I did, and it is better. Bastard.

All my mother did was complain. She moaned about the weather and the television, which was on all the time, even though it was rotten. She blamed the oldman, called him a waster, a liar, a thief and a drunk, especially a drunk.

'What have I done?' she asked no one. 'What have I done to be married to a drunkard?'

The other thing she did was worry, mostly about the oldman, wondering where he was and what he was doing, hoping he was all right, which he always was.

When he'd come back it was great for a while, but it always got worse, always; it always got worse. So we stopped believing, even before we went to the home, we stopped believing my mother and her stories, the oldman and his promises. In the end when my granny said I could go and stay with her I just went and never bothered.

It wasn't bad. She drank, but it wasn't as bad as with the oldman. She'd make soup and we'd have to eat it. 'Stick to you ribs,' she'd say. That's all we ate, soups and stews and mince; porridge in the mornings.

She'd get her bottle and sit by the fire, singing songs about the Heilans, seeing faces and things in the flames, telling us about her granny and what she'd told her, always asking how a poor old widow woman was to cope with this life and its troubles.

'A vale of tears,' she'd say. 'A vale of tears.' Then she'd sigh, straighten her apron and read her favourite book. It had no covers. She'd open it on any page, read with an old magnifying glass and say, 'That's right,' then tell us the story up till then and carry on reading out loud till she fell asleep. The book was called *How The Sheik Won His Bride*. I've asked; it isn't in the library.

She died.

I got up one morning and knew it as soon as I looked at her. Her jaws were sunk and her eyes were staring. I got the man next door and he sent for the polis who bought me sweets and said it would be all right.

That was the start of the social workers. They asked me what I wanted then sent me to a home. They told me the old dear couldn't cope, that I was beyond parental control, there was trouble with the sisters and all sorts of other stuff. I was taken into care.

All the homes smelled the same, polish, pish and cooking. The first home was temporary, but the bigger the buildings became the more you knew you were stuck. Where else could you go? No one wanted you and that was that.

The staff were the same. One or two of them were all right, but they stopped when you didn't tell them why you ran away.

You could always tell the bent shots. They were hard on you at first, then started with the favours, extra helpings, cushy jobs and finding ways of being alone with you. The first time he tried it I refused. Then he put me on the coal, working in the cellars, filling buckets and humping them round a big old building for two fucken months, chopping wood and getting into a row if it wasn't done. Then someone else got it and I was put on polishing the floors.

That was when he tried it a second time. I thought so fucken what and let him. He could do what he liked. I didn't care. Everybody did it anyway. It wasn't that bad and no matter how bad it was it wasn't as bad as when you refused.

Everybody knew. If you were seen with McKillop it was rumpy pumpy. He got barred from the Scouts because he was bent, so if you were seen with him it was, How's your arse? He left you alone for a while if a new boy came or if he fancied somebody else. All you did was let him do it and it was okay after that.

Who could you tell? No one would believe you. They'd have a daft tribunal where you'd have to tell what happened with him sitting there, knowing what he'd do to you afterwards. If he was found not guilty he carried on working in the same place with you and everybody else. 'What proof do you have that this incident occurred?' they'd ask. What kind of proof can you give for something like that. Who would they believe, him or you?

You didn't want anyone to know anyway. The first time it happened I wanted to hide.

They asked if I ran because of my family. I had two brothers older than me and one younger, one sister older and three younger, eight of us and the lassies in trouble. The oldest was six when I was born and I was seven when the last was born, so what would I want to see them for? I never even knew where the half of them were. We got split up.

Then they asked if I wanted to see my parents and me believing the oldman was dead and her as well. She sent me to the home in the first place because she couldn't cope. They must be dead by now.

There was only one reason for running away. The first time I got caught, McKillop said, 'Welcome home,' and made me polish the dorm floors, on my own. When everyone else was having supper, he came up to see how I was getting on and that was it, rumpy pumpy.

The fourth time I worked out I could stay away longer if I had a job. I'd be better off with money.

It took a while, but I wasn't afraid of asking. Someone took me on making tea and running messages. He gave me money to take to the bank. I took it to London.

It didn't last long. Everything was dear, I didn't know anyone, didn't know where to go, couldn't find anyplace right. After two days the polis chased me out the railway station and I got the bus back.

The best job I had was washing dishes. I really liked that job. You worked away on your own, nobody bothered and you got your meals. It was in this place called The Firebird with a Greek cook Stavros who hardly ever bothered me, except to shout when he'd lose his temper because there wasn't any plates.

It was hard keeping up. Everybody wanted dishes at once. Stavros made it up to me if he shouted. He'd give me bits of raw meat, steak, and tell me to cook it for myself. I didn't know what to do with it so I asked him for a bit of chicken.

I threw the meat at a crowd of dogs and watched them fight over it. The meat got all dirty, but they didn't care, they still ate it.

It was Stavros that said I could sleep in the restaurant. He said if I got caught he'd deny he told me. Fair enough. I got away with it for a couple of nights. They found out and I got the sack.

I tried another couple of places but they told me I'd need to improve my appearance. I didn't know where to go to buy clothes. I'd no money anyway. I always wore what I got at the home. If I needed new clothes I went and I got them.

Fuck trying to figure if it's nice or if it matches. What did they mean, improve my appearance? They could have told me what they meant. I asked a girl I met on the bus and she just laughed. Right now I'm wearing a brown jacket with greeny-blue stripes, a red and white pullover, a checked shirt, sort of grey trousers, blue socks and black shoes.

What's wrong with that?

Last time I ran I met wee Sonny.

He looked like a scarecrow, a rat or something. His hair was always straight back as if it growed that way, except when it was long and a lump used to hang across his brow which seemed very big, but probably wasn't big at all, it was just the way his hair grew backwards. He had funny eyes. One of them never looked straight at you; sometimes to one side and sometimes to the other, it looked the way a bird does. His squinty eyes made us think he was evil, especially when he walked funny, with his head sort of bent forward and his back in a humph.

I never even recognised him when I saw him. 'Hey. You,' he said. 'Joseph Bonner.' It was funny to hear my real name after all that time.

'You don't even remember me, do you? Stupid bastard.'

'I do so remember you.'

'What's my name?'

'I forget.'

'And where did you see me?'

'I forget that as well.'

'Peter MacDonald. They used to call us Popeye. We were in Wilson together.'

'I remember you now.'

'Daft bastard. What you doing here?'

We were in the Job Centre. I was looking for work and they told me the usual, nothing doing. I stayed in for a heat.

'Come on,' said Sonny. 'I know where there's work.'

This was in Manchester or someplace, Birmingham maybe. The Job Centre was in the middle of town, easy to find. All the way to the place, he asked where I stayed and what I'd been doing, stuff like that. He took me to a site, like a big work.

'This is the drill,' he said. 'You wait here. I'll do the talking. Okay.'

I don't know what he said, but the man came out of the shed and looked at me.

'Looks kind of young,' he said.

'He's old enough to start. He's the same age as me, but look at the strength on him. Look at his size. We've just arrived. We've no place to stay and we'll no be here long. Honest.'

He just kept talking till the man gave us a start. He got a sub as well, ten quid each.

'This is what we do,' he said. 'We'll get a room with your money and tea and stuff with mine. Then we'll do the missions and get our dinner. We'll steal the rest and get set up.'

I don't know how he did it, but we were set up.

We got a room. He knew every hand-out in the place. He knew where to go for food, clothes, shoes and he even knew the good Social Security offices, which takes some doing.

He was a wonderful thief. He got us everything. He knew what picture halls you could skip into; he never bought a fag, just asked for a smoke. He even asked for money.

He just kept at it, never stopped. He'd go down to the station, ask and keep on asking till he got what he wanted, fags, money whatever it was.

'They feel sorry for me,' he said. 'They take one look and feel sorry for me, so I make sure I look like death warmed up. You've got to learn to live off the land. Everybody thinks I need looking after.'

The foreman liked him because he was always cheery and did what he was told That's how he got called Sonny, short for Sonny Boy, because he was young looking.

'Zak's a daft name,' he said. 'If you want to change your name you should pick a name that means something. Nobody knows what Zak means. It doesn't mean anything. Did McKillop fuck you?'

'No.'

'He did so, everybody knew what was going on.'

'Why are you asking?'

'Just want to know.'

'How? Did he ride you as well?'

'I'm going to get that bastard. If it's the last thing I do,

I'm definitely going to get him.'

He just said it as if he was asking for something in a shop. He never made a big deal. He just said it.

We worked away fine.

It was good. Sonny was an easy going sort of bloke who never ever was upset or flustered. It felt good being with him. I felt everything was going to be all right.

You should have seen him on that site. Before the week was out he had guys bringing in sandwiches, giving him money, all that.

I enjoyed the work. It was good, working in the open air, stripped to the waist, getting a sweat going.

Sonny never did a hand's turn. He did nothing. He was always doing something else, going to get something that was needed for a job, or making the tea. It was all worked out.

When the job was finished the guys gave him money and told him where to go for work.

'We're quitting this,' he said. 'We've got what we wanted.'

He was carrying a black training bag.

'What is it?'

'Something I had made.'

'A machine?'

'A trap. Listen, are you with me or not?'

'Sure.'

'How much have you got?'

'What you gave me.'

I forgot to say that Sonny handled everything. He took care of the rent, bought the food and whenever I wanted money for fags or that, he fixed me up. I never went short.

He stopped walking, dead in the street and he grabbed my lapel. People were looking. He didn't care.

'Just because I look this way doesn't mean I'm daft. It doesn't mean I haven't got feelings, I'm not something for McKillop to come into; and that's what he did, he used me, made me feel dirty, cheap and ashamed. He made me feel the way I fucken look. He couldn't have wanted me because I was nice. I know because he didn't pretend. He never kidded on it was something it wasn't. I knew what it was and I knew how I felt. Every time, every fucken time he did it, he never did what he did to the other boys. He never told me I was nice. He never said I had nice eyes, nice hair or a nice body. He never gave me money or a cushy job. He never even tried to make me feel good about it. He just said, Come on then. I leaned over the bed, he rubbed the Vaseline into my arse and that was it; just the sound of him and the soreness, the shudder when he came. He wiped his prick and walked away, never said anything. At first I thought he felt the same as me; that what he was doing made him feel what I felt and that was how he couldn't look at me. Then I heard him with somebody else. I don't need to know what he was like with you. He'd love you, big strong boy; am I right, eh? I said, am I right?'

'He said I was strong.'

'Did he dress you up?'

'He gave me a leather jacket.'

'And took it off you when he was done. Did he take any pictures?'

'Just the ones that came when they were taken.'

'What were you wearing?'

'Just the jacket.'

'Did he give you other stuff?'

'Underpants and things. I forget.'

'I know what he'd be like with you, and I know what you'd be like with him. You wouldn't let it bother you. Part of your survival technique, eh; do what they want you to do. Please them. Well, it's time to choose, Mister Zak. You're with me or against him. If you're with me, you're going to help me get McKillop.'

'If you like.'

'What the fuck does that mean? How did you feel when he came? Do you remember wiping the Vaseline away and finding his come running down your leg? Do you remember what that was like?'

It was a long time ago. I didn't say anything. Sonny must have thought I remembered, because he nodded his head.

We had a cup of tea and went to the pictures. We got fish suppers on the way home and he told me what we were going to do.

'We've got some money, nearly two hundred quid.'

'Jesus Christ.'

'Shut up. We need more. We'll get it. Working's made you pretty fit, but you've got to get fitter. So from tonight there's no more fags for you and I. We'll travel north, see how the land lies and get him.'

'What do we need the money for?'

'To reward ourselves when we've done it.'

'Are we going to kill him?'

'Don't be stupid.'

'What then?'

'Give him a fright.'

He told me the rules.

'Dead simple,' he said. 'Do the rules or I'll do you. This is a mission we're on. When you're on a mission there's no messing around, no room for being wrong or fucking about. So, if anything goes wrong it'll be your fault and you will suffer. I'll sort you right out, so you'd better get it right.'

'What's the rules?'

'Rule Number One, no bevvy; Rule Number Two, no gambling; Rule Number Three, no women; Rule Number Four, no blagging; Rule Number Five, no polis; get the message, no nothing till we get McKillop. When we get him you can do what you like. All your needs will be taken care of. If you find it hard, think how nice it'll be when we've finished.'

'What are we going to do to him?'

'Sort him out.'

'How?'

'Wait and see. Tomorrow, we're off. Going north. Off to Glasgow.'

He wakened me at six o'clock. I don't know how he did it, but he could get up at any time he liked, as if he had a wee alarm clock inside his brain.

Everything was packed and ready. He told me to be quiet, not to disturb anybody, especially the landlord who would be wanting his rent. We left the key in the door.

It took us a while to come up the road. Drivers don't like stopping for two guys. Two lassies no problem, a girl on her own and they're queuing up, but they think two guys are going to rob them.

We did all right, though. One driver took us from just outside Preston to Motherwell. Sonny told him our money was knocked and we'd got beaten up by daft National Front skinheads who don't like Jocks in England, and the guy bought us a meal, sausage, egg and chips, tea, bread and butter. Then he gave us twenty fags each, Embassy Regal. Sonny sold them cause we'd stopped smoking.

We got a room in Garnethill, by Charing Cross. The Social paid, gave us an immediate payment and money for moving. Sonny just sat there and got it, every fucken thing, he was into everything, could get money out of anybody.

Then we started the rounds of the missions, Trotters, the soup run, the Sally Army, all that, the start of a really good time for me because I felt better than I'd ever felt before. I was off the booze, I wasn't smoking and was eating well. Sonny made me exercise. I had to build up to it, but after a wee while I was running a couple of miles a day and could lift three of these big weights on the end of a barbell ten times from the ground to the top of my head as well as do the wee ones about thirty times or more with each arm.

'Let's go,' he said one night.

'Where?'

'Never mind.'

We went for a walk round town. All the time Sonny was talking.

'The trouble with you is that you're used to getting things done for you. I used to be like that, but I broke the habit. Had to; started learning to live for myself. This society doesn't give people like you any initiative. All you're good for is working, hiring out your labour.'

'I'm all right, Sonny. I don't mind.'

'I know you don't. You'd probably be lost any other way. Look at how you were when I met you and look at you now. All I've done is give you a bit of an incentive. I've looked after you better than anybody. That's because you're what I wanted. It didn't happen by accident. I picked you, specially. No one else saw the potential I saw. I picked you and trained you and now you're going to work for me, because you've got incentive, same as me. You want to get back at him for what he did, same as I do, don't you?'

'Uh-hu.'

'Knew it. There were other guys, but when I saw you I knew you were right. I've been waiting. I knew you'd want to get McKillop too. This society needs people like me, who have a desire to do something, find a way to do it then get it done. People like you are there to do it. Where would you be without us? You'd starve. Everybody knows it, but I did it. Men get raped too, but you never hear a word about it.'

I hadn't noticed where we were going. We were by the bus

station.

'Look around you,' Sonny said. 'Tomorrow night, we work. This time tomorrow we'll be finished. Tonight you get an extra incentive to do a good job. Look around you. Take your pick. Tell me which one you want.'

Women were standing on street corners and in doorways, smiling at the cars: whores.

'Any one?'

'Whatever you like.' We walked around looking. 'Who's it to be?'

'I don't know. Any one will do.'

'Thought so,' he said. 'Come on. I'll get one for you as a wee reward. We've got one thing to check and then we're through.'

There was a big Post Office place near the station in a square. Vans were moving in and out and Sonny told me to wait. He went up to a guy who was loading a van: 'Is Jack McKillop around?' he asked.

'McKillop on?' the guy shouted to someone.

'Tea break.'

'It's okay,' said Sonny. 'We'll see him tomorrow night.'

'How did you know he worked there?' I asked.

'If you want to find someone bad enough, you can do it. I found out by asking. I asked everybody I met who knew him. Last time I was up here I found out. I check up every now and then. I saw him once. I was standing on the corner and he walked past, never even recognised me.'

The rest of the way home he was quiet, never said much, just asked if I wanted a fish supper. I ate it in the room, but when we were in bed he said, 'No wanking. You'll need your strength for tomorrow night.'

That reminded me. I thought about the whores, just standing there, they'd go with anybody.

When I wakened in the morning Sonny wasn't there. He came back in the afternoon with some rolls and we had something to eat, watching the horses on the telly. Around nine o'clock at night he got his training bag down from the top of the wardrobe and opened it up.

'Seen this?' he said.

It was a contraption, like a cage, covered in wire with straps at the end of it. One of the ends opened.

'It'll do,' he said.

'Where did you get it?'

'I got it made in a factory the way I wanted.'

'What is it?'

'A wee surprise for Mr McKillop.'

On the way to the Post Office he bought a tube of cream cheese and all the way down the road he was smiling. We went round the lane at the back of the Post Office.

'Do you need to do anything to get your strength up?'

'Not really.'

'I thought you needed to warm up.'

'That's only if you're going to exercise or lift weights.'

'Take off your jacket and your pullover.'

It was cold.

'Run on the spot till I tell you to stop.'

I ran for ages. My face was all red and I was peching a bit.

'Right,' said Sonny. 'Get these on and tell me when you've got your breath back.'

And just before we went to the Post Office he said, 'I'll tell you when. All you have to do is hold him.'

He went in and asked for McKillop. We waited a while and this old guy I never even recognised came out and looked around him.

'Somebody wanting me?' he asked

I was trying to remember if this was McKillop. I wasn't sure. This guy looked quite fat, with a beer belly. He was baldy and McKillop wasn't like that. This guy had a moustache.

'You're Jack McKillop, eh?' said Sonny. 'Used to work at Wilson House?'

'What about it?'

'I want to make sure I've got the right guy. You know Rab Gibson?'

'Who the hell are you?'

'Rab wants to see you, says it's important.'

I remembered Rab Gibson, a wee guy, skinny with blond hair, a good runner. I think McKillop liked him.

'What did he send you for? How could he no come for himself?'

'Ask him when you see him. He told me to ask for Jack McKillop at the George Square Post Office. I've done what he asked and that's it.'

'Is he all right?'

'What do you think?' Sonny asked me. 'Do you think he's

all right?'

I didn't know what to say. He should have told me. I didn't know. I just looked at Sonny, then at McKillop, then back at Sonny.

'Does that answer your question?' asked Sonny. 'Let's go. I think Rab made a mistake. This guy isn't interested.'

'Where is he?'

'I thought you'd know that.'

'I haven't seen him for a while.'

'As far as I know he's sleeping rough. Last time I saw him he was using a skipper in Maryhill.'

'I haven't any money.'

'He never mentioned money. He said to tell you he wanted to see you. If you want us to take you there, we can do that, but I don't know the address. The way he spoke I thought you'd know where he was.'

'I don't finish till after two.'

'Okay then, meet us at the back at two.'

'Where?'

'Under the bridge at Belmont Street.'

'It'll be nearer half two by the time I get there.'

'That's fine. One of us will be there. We'll tell Rab you're coming.'

'Fine. Do you know if he's been using?'

'He's hitting up with kit.'

McKillop shook his head. He turned away, went back to work.

Sonny didn't say much walking to Belmont Street. When we got near there, he said, 'The bastard never even recognised us. Just shows you, eh.'

He sat under the bridge for ages.

'When he gets here, grab him from the back and hold him.' He lit a cigarette. 'Make sure his arms don't move and I'll do the rest. If you hit him with something that'd be best. Not too hard, though, enough to make him dizzy. I don't want him to see you, so hide till he gets here. Okay.'

'No problem.'

'There'd better be no problems. We'll get one shot at this. When I tell you to run, beat it. Get to hell out of here. He's going to yell hard enough to bring the place down. Go back to the room. Everything's there, and a wee surprise as well. Okay.'

'What're you going to do?'

'I'm going to enjoy myself.'

We were there for ages. I started whistling and Sonny told me to shut up, so we just stood there, listening to the sounds the water made dripping down from the bridge. Everything echoed. Apart from the dripping noise and the traffic passing over the bridge there was nothing except we sometimes heard people passing, someone laughing or a drunk man singing, but nobody came down the steps.

'Right,' said Sonny.

He took the cream cheese from his pocket and spread it onto a bit of cardboard. He put it in the cage and went down to the river.

'What'll I do if McKillop comes?'

'I'll be back before he gets here.'

He came back laughing, sort of giggling and snorting to himself.

'A beauty,' he said. 'A big fucken beauty.'

There was a rat in the cage, eating the cheese. Then it started on the cardboard.

I don't know how he knew. I can't work out how he timed it, but as soon as he was back with the rat he told me to hide.

'He'll be here soon,' he said.

He told me where to hide and what to do. He told me McKillop would come down the steps.

About five minutes or ten minutes later, McKillop stood at the edge of the tunnel.

'Anybody there?' he shouted.

'This way,' said Sonny.

'Christ,' he said. 'It's dark in here.'

'We don't have far to go.'

'Is your mate with Rab?'

'Uh-hu. He's strung out.'

That was my signal. They were just out of the tunnel. I hit McKillop on the back of the head with a stone. I didn't think he'd go down. He staggered a bit. I hit him again and he went down this time. I did what Sonny told me to do. I held both his arms in a bear hug from the back. Sonny undid McKillop's trousers and tied the cage around his legs and between his knees. He smeared McKillop's balls with the cheese. The rat was clawing at the cage. I let McKillop go.

'Hold him,' said Sonny. 'Hold on to the bastard.'

There was a scream. McKillop must have come round and saw the rat, with its teeth in the wire, trying to get at the cheese on McKillop's balls.

I never heard anybody scream so much in all my life. Never. He wriggled away from me. I couldn't have held him, even if I wanted to. He was screaming and kicking, pushing himself backwards with his hands, trying to get away from the cage which was tied to him and all the time he's screaming and crying with the rat going daft and biting the wire.

'Remember me?' said Sonny. 'Do you know who I am?'

I just stood there, looking.

'Get out of here,' said Sonny. 'On you go. Beat it.'

I ran along the tunnel. I was scared, though I didn't know what I was scared of; I suppose I thought other rats could come. The last thing I saw before I ran up the stairs was McKillop trying to stand up. I could hear the rat clawing in the cage. Sonny pushed McKillop back down into a puddle, shouting his name and telling him who he was and laughing, laughing really loudly. That was the first time I heard him laugh. I ran up the stairs.

Belmont Street was well lit. There was no one around. From the street you could hear McKillop screaming. The sound of Sonny laughing and McKillop screaming was like drunk men fighting, then it died down.

I went back to the room to wait for Sonny. I knew before I put on the light that somebody was there. She said her name was Trudi. She knew who I was and said Sonny had sent her.

When I wakened in the morning she was gone. Just a smell on the pillow to let you know she'd been there. I watched television and waited for Sonny. Then I noticed his stuff wasn't there. Everything of mine, my clothes and things were where I left them. There was money in my holdall, two hundred pounds.

That night I went down to Charing Cross and got a fish supper, some fags and a couple of cans of beer. It was good to be smoking again.

I stuck it out for nearly a week. Sonny never came back. I didn't know who to pay the rent to and couldn't get a job anyway, so I moved out one night when I was sure he wouldn't be back. I never saw him again, never heard of him; don't know what happened.

James McGonigal

APPROACHING SPRING: 50 paces
i.m. R. Gomez de la Serna

In the cauld blast
Each desperate tree
cradles the ghost of a sea.
Shoosh, stop your girning!

The morning after
What they reflect on
all night makes streetlamps stagger
half-blind at first light.

The two travellers
From outer islands
friends arrive, eat, tell their tales:
'... monstrous ... waves ... bereft ...'

Winter daze
The world drinks too much:
crazily spinning from gold
to gloom to blackout.

Dead stop
Listen. Lift it up
to your ear. Shake. Still nothing
from the skull's stopped clock.

Waking on a rainy morning
Day hauls up its net
and we're in it, gasping and
fighting for darkness!

Flood warning
With dripping hair, earth
reaches for her towel of light ...
Och, it's soaking too.

A sharp night
That blade of new moon
shaving the star-stubbled cheek
of a wintry sky.

Field study
Peck at the problem,
little birds, solve the senseless
equation of frost.

Lazy x 2
Sunny Saturday –
a blue sabbatical: we
doze, kiss, talk, kiss, doze ...

Lost pages of frost
Which took all night long
to perfect. 'Too perfect,' says
the sun. 'Burn the lot!'

Rhododendrons
Those buds tight as fists
keep their purple gashes well
hidden till Easter.

A red sky at night
O red-rimmed eyelid
drooping over the cooling
stove of the city.

Bedtime
Slide between ice-cold
sheets, for your sleighride through night's
landscape of white dreams.

Feeling our way through fog
The world's been transcribed
into braille: we grasp at it
with thick grey gloves on.

Burnt offerings
From the motorway's
altar, sniff the incense of
civilisation.

Still waters
The heart of the loch
is stunned that we have just glimpsed
its most secret joy.

Good shot
Year by year the bow
of summer fires off flights of
swallows at our hearts!

Swan's way
See how the first line
of the canal's long poem
starts: a fancy S.

Still searching
Dead leaves that blackbirds
flick aside: a moment's flight
for abandoned wings.

The dumb waiter
Who spread tablecloths
over the fields, and dropped plates
where puddles were? Frost.

Space
In the sky's graveyard
the moon's the oldest tombstone.
Can't quite ... read ... the date.

Foggiest notion
Back to the womb: we're
floating, or else the earth is.
What's time now? Where's space?

Turning night into day
What makes the world rock
from dark to light and back? Two
billion dreaming heads.

The road home
Is this the wrong road?
The house seems smaller: soaked through
by mist has it shrunk?

Waking from a dream of eagles
A piece of paper
vexed by the wind like a bird
mortally wounded.

Dawn exposure
I tug the blind's cord
like an ancient camera:
trees; sepia sky.

No exit
How can we leave here?
The maps of our homeland all
have blue and red veins.

Thinning out
Trunks laid in churned earth;
smoke rising from lopped branches
piled like dead men's clothes.

Snowdrops
Dazed by spring winds: look –
palefaced children birling on
a merry-go-round.

Utility Room
Enter the shrine and
offer your chaos to these
household gods. Press START.

Here's looking at you, kid
Heavy lids of cloud
open to reveal two pools
of blue. Good heavens!

In a city back court
Lichened branches barely
swaying in this wind. Listen:
wood pigeons crooning.

At this time of year
From shapeless pouches
gardens stuff their pipes with shreds
of leaves. Light up. Puff.

Aristotle on a winter's night
Raw wind. A quarter moon.
Forby the polis only
beasts and heroes walk.

Over the sea to sky
Rags of cloud like waves
in the sky's estuary:
we stare out. Forth.

Gift of the garb
Dawn. What will it be?
The hills lift a suit from their
all-weather wardrobe.

The kiss of fate
Fake lashes falling
from night's wicked eye, crows sheer
off, brushing day's cheek.

Journey
Windscreen wiped clean, then
covered over with raindrops –
these generations.

Surprised by snow
Houses and people
pull on an extra layer
and stare blankly out.

A last look
Bleak days. Snow faces
gaze up at us, vanishing
into earth's dank ditch.

White hair overnight
Aristocrat moon
placing her head below that
viaduct's poised blade.

Early light
Even abandoned
cars by the roadside are blessed
by the hand of frost.

Into the dark
Illuminated
buildings sail off like ships on
waves of history.

After many days
From the sorrowing
earth are squeezed these purple tears
of polyanthus.

No reply
Unanswered letters
adrift on my table: leaves
the four winds blew in.

Night duty
Nights when the moon spent
hours studying x-rays of
her own damaged heart.

Ascendant
Pine logs were sparking
high in our chimney: their smoke
made heaven's eyes sting.

The path
Once he discovered
that path to the forest pool
he walked nowhere else.

Way of the world
Limping towards spring: one
limb of darkness dragged after
each footstep of light.

John C. McIntyre

A RIOT OF YELLOW BUTTERFLIES

That morning Gregorio went fishing. He wandered up and down his favourite stretch of the river-bank but didn't have too much luck. By late morning he'd managed to catch just two catfish. They were barely big enough for Maria to make a decent fish-stew.

By eleven o'clock it was getting too hot to move around and fish. He went in for a swim. As he sat drying off on the river bank he watched a single yellow butterfly float down out of the trees and settle on his left ankle. Then as he started to walk back to the town he was aware of about a dozen butterflies fluttering around his bare shoulders and above his head. He didn't pay any attention to them until he came to the first houses and met old Anselmo.

'Hi, Gregorio.'

'Hello, Anselmo.'

'You've been fishing?'

'Yes. I've only caught two. I don't think Maria will be too pleased.'

'For the woman of the house the man never brings in enough.'

'I suppose you're right.'

'Gregorio, what's with the butterflies?'

'What's that, Anselmo?'

'The yellow butterflies. Can't you see the butterflies?'

Gregorio looked up and just above his head was a great cloud of yellow butterflies.

'Yeah, I saw a few following me from the river.'

'A few? Gregorio, you've got hundreds there.'

'Well, I can't do anything about it. Maybe if Maria could catch a few, we could have them with the catfish. Catfish flavoured with butterflies ought to be quite tasty. Well, I'll be seeing you, Anselmo.'

'Gregorio, you're really touched. I'll be seeing you.'

''Bye, Anselmo.'

* * *

Gregorio started off again, followed by the whirling butterflies. A couple of boys had been watching from a house-door and began to tag along after him. The tall stringy one with the flashing teeth was Pedro, the oldest son of his best friend, the baker. The other was Moisés, the candle-maker's youngest boy. These two lads were always on the lookout for mischief, and called over a few of their friends to see the butterflies.

Two or three blocks later Gregorio had fifteen or sixteen children in tow. He could hear them all chattering excitedly behind him about the yellow butterflies. The buzz of noise began to run ahead of Gregorio and the heads of people out shopping and strolling were turning even before he reached them. A couple of times he pointed up at the butterflies just above his head, grimaced and shrugged his shoulders, disclaiming responsibility for the strange event.

By the time he was cutting across the square towards the tiny little white-washed house that he and Maria rented from the mayor, he had a gawping crowd of children and grown-ups trailing along behind him and his swarm of butterflies.

'Gregorio! Stand still! Don't move, or I'll shoot! Stand still. That's an order!'

Gregorio stopped. The podgy sergeant ran over towards him with his pistol at the ready. As the sergeant came up close, Gregorio could see the greasy sweat trickling down the sergeant's flushed face and staining the armpits of his dirty uniform. Gregorio reminded himself not to be too clever with his answers: the sergeant had a reputation for having a nasty temper and for being foul-mouthed and very brutal. The sergeant spat out the words:

'What the frigging hell do you think you're doing?'

'I'm going home for lunch.'

'What are all these people doing? Why are they all following you?'

'I don't know. I think they're watching the butterflies.'

'Where did you get the frigging butterflies?'

'They were at the river. They've been following me.'

Now that Gregorio had stopped walking, the butterflies were settling all across his naked shoulders and back.

'Get rid of those shitty butterflies!' screamed the sergeant.

'Eh?'

'Get rid of them! Now! Right now!'

The fat little sergeant pointed the pistol directly at Gregorio's lower belly. Gregorio began to wave his arms frantically, flapping the fishing cane and the two catfish at the butterflies. They scattered for a second and then gradually came together again in a great flutter of wings above Gregorio's head. The sergeant quivered and trembled with rage and waved his pistol like a man demented.

'Gregorio, I'm warning you. Get rid of them or I'll arrest you. You're causing a disturbance.'

'Sergeant, I can't control them. You know that.'

The sergeant turned to the crowd and shouted at them. 'Right! That's it! Everybody! Off the streets! Now! Gregorio, you get your miserable ass over to the jail.'

The crowd, which a moment previously had been cheerful and light-hearted, turned sullen as it began to move from the square.

At the jail door the sergeant stopped for a second, let the fluttering butterflies gather together just above Gregorio's head, then rushed Gregorio through the doorway and slammed the door shut to keep them out. He shoved Gregorio into a dingy cell at the back of the prison and sent one of his soldiers over to doña Alejandrina Cervantes's pleasure palace to report the disturbance to the magistrate and the lieutenant.

Within five minutes the butterflies had found their way in through the barred window of Gregorio's little cell at the back of the prison. When the magistrate and the lieutenant arrived an hour and a half later, Gregorio was dozing in the driest corner of the dank cell, his shoulders, arms, legs and ankles covered over with a mass of quivering yellow wings.

* * *

Gregorio's shoulders were still covered in butterflies when he was pushed into the interrogation room.

'Sit down, Gregorio.'

'Thank you, your honour.'

The magistrate was sitting on the other side of a plain table. He lit up a cigarette. He didn't offer one to Gregorio. The lieutenant leaned languidly against the far wall, looking at Gregorio with cold, cold eyes, as if he were already a piece of dead meat. Gregorio shivered, sending some of the butterflies spinning about the room.

'What were you up to this morning?'

'Nothing. I went fishing, that's all.'

'You know that's not true, Gregorio. We think that you were really trying to stir up trouble. Who were your accomplices? Who helped you organise that mess this morning? You must tell me.'

'I didn't organise anything, your honour. I went fishing, had a swim, then I came home. The butterflies followed me back. I don't know why they followed me. I think the people followed the butterflies. I couldn't stop them.'

'You know this kind of thing is forbidden under the martial law regulations?'

'Butterflies?'

'Don't be so damned insolent! The crowd is what's forbidden! The government doesn't allow any meeting of more than ten people. You know that perfectly well.'

'Yes, I know that, your honour.'

'Well, then, you've broken the law.'

'But I didn't get all those people together. It wasn't my idea, honest.'

'Are you mixed up with the guerrillas? Are you maybe mixed up with those union people?'

'No, your honour, of course I'm not. You know me. I'm not interested in politics. I'm a banana cutter – when I can get work.'

'That's a political statement! You *are* against the government! Admit it, you little radical asshole!'

'Please, your honour! I'm just a banana cutter, a day labourer. There's no work right now. I just went fishing. The butterflies followed me back to the square. I don't know why they did. That's all I know.'

The magistrate and the lieutenant whispered together for a few moments. Gregorio could see the lieutenant rubbing his right thumb and forefingers together. Gregorio sighed. He could see that they would be looking for money.

'Gregorio, we think you were organising some kind of demonstration. That's very serious.'

'Your honour, honest. I wasn't.'

'You're a liar, Gregorio. So we're going to fine you 500 pesos. Just get the money and give it to the lieutenant. Don't give it to anybody else, mind you, just the lieutenant, and we'll let you go free – this time.'

'Your honour, we don't even have five pesos in the house.'

'Borrow it from your friends, then. You had plenty of them round you this morning.'

'They're all just as poor as me.'

'So you refuse to pay?'

'Your honour, I cannot pay. I'm really sorry.'

'Gregorio, you're stupid. Fifteen days in jail! Sergeant! Lock this troublesome bastard up! And don't let him have any special privileges!'

* * *

It was a real struggle for Maria, but she managed to keep Gregorio fed while he was in jail. She did get a lot of help from his friends – a few fish here, a bit of meat there. Somehow she managed.

Gregorio became quite fond of the butterflies, though they disappeared on the third day. He had complained of being dirty and the guards took him out to the inner courtyard of the prison and hosed him down. For a laugh they stood him against the section of wall pock-marked with bullets from old executions. Gregorio, dripping with water and trembling with fear, couldn't get back to the cell quickly enough. His butterflies never came back.

He heard from Maria that the lieutenant, the sergeant and three soldiers had searched the house, almost wrecking it as they searched for guns and what Maria called 'clandine literature'. They said that they'd be back. Gregorio tried to tell the lieutenant that he and Maria couldn't read or write, that there were no books or pamphlets in the house, but the officer waved him away with the comment that the men were only carrying out their orders.

Maria also reported to him that the parish priest – old Francisco Javier of the Most Holy Spilled Blood of Christ the Saviour – had been foaming and fulminating from the pulpit at Sunday Mass against the 'yellow peril' that was threatening to 'tear apart the fabric of a well-ordered and truly Catholic society guaranteed here in our beloved fatherland by the most loyal and faithful support of all right-thinking men and women.'

The parishioners – even the little ladies in the perpetual black of their lonely widowhoods – dozed through this sermon, as they dozed through all the old priest's rantings and perorations. They only woke up and paid attention about twice a year, when they saw him totter up into the pulpit carrying a steaming cup of chocolate that the altar-boy brought him fresh from the sacristy. It was then that he threatened to bless the chocolate three times, drink it and levitate before their disbelieving and heretical eyes to prove the truth of the Ascension of Christ and of the Assumptions of the Blessed Virgin Mary and of Remedios the Beautiful. Some parishioners never quite gave up hope of witnessing the old curate's first levitation, wondering fondly if the church dome would open up to ease his final passage to heaven.

Gregorio also heard from Maria that the doctor, a well-known radical who couldn't be locked up because he was the only doctor for thirty miles in any direction, had been through his three reference books and the pharmacist's and the schoolteacher's worn encyclopaedias to try to find a scientific explanation for the crowd of yellow butterflies. The doctor refused to recognise what was being called the 'miracle of the butterflies', and wanted to talk to Gregorio at length when he got out of prison.

Gregorio didn't much like the sound of the word 'miracle' either. Maria also told him that the customers at the billiards parlour – who hadn't had a game for months, not since some thieving mean-spirited bastard had broken in and made off with the three balls – were saying that Gregorio clearly had some very special power, so they were going to hire him as soon as he got out of prison to track down not the thief, just the billiard balls. They were desperate to get their balls back. Gregorio had no idea how they expected him to manage it. And as and when he failed to find the billiard balls, he didn't like to think of what the irate billiards players would do to him.

What with having to face new searches of his house, the accusations of the parish priest, the mad enquiries of the doctor and the pleas of the customers in the billiards parlour, Gregorio could see that he was going to have a few problems when he got out of prison.

* * *

The morning that Gregorio left prison, he went straight home with Maria and found the doctor waiting for him. Quite a number of his neighbours were standing around, welcoming him back warmly. The doctor made Gregorio sit down and go over all the details of the morning he'd caught the two catfish, then insisted on dragging Gregorio and Maria out to the river.

As they made their way out to the river, half the town seemed to be drifting in the same direction, always in groups of three or four, never in groups of more than ten, so as not to be challenged and turned back by the patrolling pairs of soldiers.

'Gregorio, show me exactly where you went in swimming that morning.'

'Just there, doctor.'

'Where all that brown gooey stuff is?'

'Just beyond it, doctor. A little downstream.'

As the doctor studied the river some of the younger children dived in and started splashing about. A couple of minutes later a few of them came out and sat down on the river bank. Within seconds yellow butterflies began to appear out of the trees and settle on their legs and shoulders. The children whooped and squealed with joy.

'There's something in the water that the butterflies like!' shouted the doctor. 'It sticks to the body while you're swimming, and then the butterflies lick it off your body when you come out.'

Gregorio remembered being hosed down in the yard of the prison.

'That's right, doctor! After the prison guards hosed me down and washed the stuff off me, the butterflies left me alone. They never came back.'

By this time all the children had tumbled into the water, coming out and waiting for great masses of butterflies to settle on their arms and legs. The younger children found the sensation of dozens of butterflies ticklish and began giggling. The hilarity spread through the crowd. Lots of the grown-ups piled into the river as well. Within a few minutes the whole crowd was howling with delight at the wondrous beauty of the yellow butterflies absolutely covering the arms, legs and even their whole bodies.

'Let's go and tell the magistrate and the lieutenant how it happened. They should never have jailed Gregorio. He couldn't help the butterflies.'

Giggling and laughing, the crowd began to head for town. The children ran all over the place, followed by their individual spirals of swirling butterflies.

As they turned the last corner to head for the square, the first children suddenly came up against two rows of soldiers and policemen, one row kneeling in front of the other, all of them armed with rifles. The children at the back and round the corner could not see what was happening in front and pushed the first rows of their friends almost right up against the first armed line.

'Halt! This is an order! Halt or we fire!' shouted the lieutenant.

The children at the back could not make out the command and continued to push forward.

'First squad! One volley! Over their heads! Fire!'

The clatter of the shots brought the parents running up anxiously from behind. The children ran in terror back towards their parents. As the space just in front of the soldiers cleared, a boy could be seen lying sprawled in the middle of the street. The head lay in a great pool of blood that was spreading slowly out into a kind of halo.

It was the boy called Pedro, the baker's son, the gangly lad with the big smile. He was dead. The soldiers kneeling in the front row had aimed to fire over the children's heads, but there were one or two taller children like Pedro hidden in the great clouds of butterflies. In the panic and chaos one of the smaller soldiers kneeling nervously in the front row had not angled his rifle steeply enough. The bullet had caught Pedro on the edge of the forehead and torn through his skull from front to back. He had been killed instantly.

An eerie silence fell, broken only by the re-cocking of the rifles and the whimpers of some of the women. The doctor knelt down and gently wrapped Pedro's head in a white linen cloth taken from a woman's shopping basket. The crowd opened up in front of Gregorio and the doctor as they carried the dead boy to his home three streets away. In spite of the doctor's best efforts, blood dripped from the dead boy's head and splashed on the street, marking their passage. Scores of yellow butterflies sat perched on the boy's bare chest as he was carried home.

Alistair Mackinnon

LAZARENE

I have a horror of cold food, coins, cheap linen
and empty rooms, my wife's warm hand
does not comfort but reminds me of
my first death-bed, my second unwailing birth.

I died to live they said
when at first I was revived.
I was more surprised than they
for I had no belief in their messiah.

Now zealots seek me out and rehearse
my encounters with Gods and ghost
and tell me my former life was
a false start to this: this a false start to the next.

But I remember nothing and now tremble
as I did not before at shadows and red devils.
I have to wait now for the more final call
knowing I am not witness to my own miracle.

I have to wait now for the most final end
knowing I was spared once – to commit what sin?

Hugh McMillan

PLAY

We sit, my son and I,
on the train from Larbert,
playing with our toys.
He has Bret the Hit Man Hart
and I have a new can of Export,
bright as a pillar box.
Haaaaaaaa he whispers, haaaaaaa,
it is the noise of the crowd in his head.
It has a large capacity, his head,
all seated, like Ibrox Park.
I myself am waiting for the plastic tag
that bears the letter X.
It is on the bottom of the can
and will win us a holiday in Barbados
at the Liver Unit of my choice.
While we play, Scotland flicks unnoticed by,
its fins of frost, trees cupping cold hands,
living rooms stiff with Sunday,
then we bounce into Glasgow.
'Still time' he says, 'still time'
and Bret lunges for a clothes line
or is it a folding body press I don't know,
I am watching foam recede from
a smooth and endless shore,
no X only a blurred reflection
of a place, a person, I should be.

Angus MacPhee

RONA

Thàinig thu –
dh'fhuirich thu greiseag ...
ach cha robh e fada.

Tha na bliadhnaichean air triall
's cha robh thu ann,
còmhla ruinn a'fàs,
am beatha
an sonas
an gaol.

Tha'm fàsach
a tha nam chridhe
far am b'àbhaist dhut a bhi,
na Mhac-talla
leis gach aisling
nach do rinn sinn.

Nuair a dh'fhalbh thu bhuainn
thubhairt boireannach rium là
gum biodh tè-bheag agamsa
gu bràth ...
is tha sin fìor,
ged a smaoin mi aig an àm
nach robh e
na cho-fhurtachd,
mar bha i'n dùil.

Ach bha ise ceart,
oir tha deich bliadhn' air fhichead
nis air triall
bho'n a bheannaich thu
ar beatha
le cho mòr do ghràdh,
is ged a tha
do pheathraichean a nis air fàs
suas gu saoghal ùr dhaibh-fhein ...

is tusa
mo chaileag-ghorm-shùileach,
agus bidh
do ghàire beag tùchail a' seinn
a nuas troimh gach oidhche
dheth mo bheath'n dràsd'
is mar a bhitheas
romham ...
gus mu dheireadh thall
gum bi thu riumsa
teann.

Translation

RONA

You came –
you stayed a while ...
but not for long.

The years have passed
and you have not been there,
to grow with us,
in life
in happiness
in love.

The emptiness
of that place in my heart
which you once filled
is echoing,
with all the dreams
we did not share.

When you had gone
a lady said to me
that I would always have
a little girl ...
and that is true,
though at the time I thought
that it was not
the comfort
she had meant.

But she was right,
for thirty years have passed,
since you so sweetly
blessed our lives
and though your sisters
now have grown
to live
lives of their own ...
you are still
my blue-eyed girl
whose husky little laugh
will ring down through the nights
of my life to come ...
till once again
I hold you in my arms.

Ruaraidh MacThòmais

TURSACHAN

Nuair a bha Alba
beagan deas air a Loidhne,
's i 'na fàsach gainmhich
le corra oasis,
cha robh sgeul air iolaire
no capall-coille;
cha robh na h-eich air tighinn,
no air falbh,
cha robh mèil caora ri cluinntinn,
's cha robh Sòdhaigh no Hiort
air an cruth a lorg,
gun luaidh air an ainm;
bha a' chreag Leòdhasach am badeigin
ged nach robh fraoch no mòine ga còmhdach;
agus b' ann fada an dèidh sin
a chlisg an Cliseam troimhn deigh
's a thòisich Beinn Nibheis a' fàs beag,
's a thogadh Tursachan Chalanais,
gun luaidh air Caisteal Dhun Eidinn;
bha eachdraidh fhathast a' feitheamh
ri tighinn nan Ceilteach
's nan Ròmanach
's nan Sasannach,
's ri taighean mòra Ghlaschu,
snaight às an t-seann ghainmhich
a chaidh 'na creig phronn.

Is dòcha gum bu chòir dhuinn bhith umhail
mu choinneamh na sìorraidheachd caillte sin,
a' cuimhneachadh nach bi cuarraidh Lingereabhaigh
ach 'na lodan là brèagh air choreigin,
's gun tèid aillse Dhun Rèidh
fo rùm mar a chaidh Cait Ghallaibh,
is luchd-poilitics cho diomain
's a bha am madadh-allaidh ann an Albainn,
ged tha sionnaich gu leòr againn fhathast.

'S an dèidh sin, an dèidh sin,
tha mi 'n dòchas nach fhalbh anail a' Ghaidheil
le ceò na mònach mu dheireadh,
's gun tog sinn tursachan
dhar linn fhìn.

Translated by Derick Thomson

STANDING STONES

When Scotland lay
a little south of the Equator,
a sandy desert
with an occasional oasis,
there were no eagles to be seen
nor capercaillies;
the horses had not come,
nor gone,
no sheep could be heard bleating,
and Soay and St Kilda
had not taken shape,
much less acquired their names;
there was Lewisian gneiss somewhere,
though not coated in heather or peat;
and it was not till long afterwards
that the Clisham burst from the ice
and Ben Nevis began to grow small,
and the Callanish Stones were set up,
not to mention Edinburgh Castle;
history still awaited
the coming of the Celts
and the Romans
and the Saxons,
and the great Glasgow mansions
carved from the ancient sand
that had turned into friable rock.

Perhaps we ought to be humble
confronting that lost eternity,
remembering that Lingerbay Quarry,
one fine day, will be a mere puddle,
and that Dounreay's cancer
will go underground as the Caithness Cats did,
with politicians as short-lived
as the wolf was in Scotland,
though we have plenty foxes still.

But still, still
I hope the Gaels' breath does not disappear
with the last peat-smoke
and that we will build standing-stones
for our own century.

John Maley

THE GHOST OF LIBERACE

The pink triangle on my lapel was a gift from
Adolf. That bastard knew the power of identity.
Do you? I've concocted a plan. It's outrageous.
I'm going to appear in Sauchiehall Street,
dressed like the ghost of Liberace. I'll whistle
at workmen, I'll wink and wiggle and waltz
to Cole Porter. I'll wield a Wildean wit. I'll
rave with Jimmy Somerville's Ruchill falsetto.
The red ribbon on my lapel was a gift from
God. Or whatever angel knows the power of mercy.
Do you think through grief we'll find a voice?
Sew our names for the world to see for good?
Do you understand that silence equals death?
Click your ruby slippers and take a deep breath.

Gordon Meade

THE SONGS OF FISH

We all know the songs
Of whales and the sonar clicks

Of bottle-nosed dolphins.
We've heard them all

On our television sets.
But there are others

We haven't heard, and
Some we'd rather forget...

The damselfish's chirp
And the minnow's purr,

The cod's lone grunt
And the haddock's whirr,

The flounder's lullaby
And the sole's lament,

The trout's apology
And the grayling's complaint,

The eel's rattle
And the conger's shake,

The zander's death march
And the herring's wake,

The stickleback's ditty
And the witch's spell,

The lumpsucker's ragtime
And the spurdog's hell,

The thornback's skiffle
And the whiting's swing,

The barbel's ballad
And the mullet's din,

The plaice's anthem
And the roach's soul,

The bass's rock
And the dace's roll,

The carp's cool jazz
And the bleak's soft psalm,

The bream's blue grass
And the dab's alarm,

The mackerel's whistle
And the shark's dry laugh,

The salmon's swan-song
And the pike's last gasp.

William Neill

UBERMENSCH

Fritskie Nitskie settin thare in his digs
Shilpit wee nyaff o a bodie that he wes,
Seeminlie gied himsel an unco buzz
Sortin us oot intil Ower-Fowk an Pigs.

The warld, said he: Born Leaders an – The Rest.
The feck o us no leaders but the latter.
For aw the glengore med him gyte's a hatter
Some mak a Prophet o yon scruntie pest.

The Ower-Fowk hae gien us monie a Gift:
Becquerel Bombs, seas fu o awkin shite,
Shipyairds gane roostie, steel mills tuim o steel.

Thay've med a muckle Ozone Hole in the lift.
But shair as daith it's The Grumphies that they'll wyte,
An chairge us aw for a moothfu o watter as weill.

Honor Patching

SOMEONE ELSE'S BODY

The Leisure Centre pool: warmth, a smell of chlorine, reflections that waver endlessly on the tiled walls. Music – there is always music playing and the lulling swish and splash of water. In the humid air, voices seem to soften and spread.

The palm was a live tree once. Now, it's dead. The jaunty-looking, green fronds that sprout from the top of its trunk are made of flexible vinyl. Here, all is artificial. But it is, oh, so warm and the music is so soothing.

Out there, through the big plate glass windows, you can see the sun shining, sometimes it may even snow, but to Rose, as she cleaves the water in a neat, relaxed crawl, it is the outside world that seems unreal. As though the people walking their dogs by the sea are actors in a film, projected on screens round the pool.

The North Road Baths, where Rose went as a child, were cold, grim, Victorian. In the ugly bathing suit she wore then, gathered into rows of green crinkles like brussels sprouts, she was driven, goose-pimpled and shivering, up the iron steps to the diving board.

The cold pinches you like icy fingers. But you have to do what grown-ups say.

As she stood on the slippery plank, the echoes would swoop and swirl from the high vaulted ceiling, like a weird song, like the music you hear in nightmares.

And you are always so cold.

At last, she would cast herself down and the steely-blue water would crash and close over her and the inside of her head would ring like a bell.

Rose has a smooth, pink swimsuit now, made with Lycra. She wears goggles to keep the smart of chlorine from her eyes. Underwater, everything is a clear bright blue, with moving lights in it, and the bottom halves of people treading the measures of a dreamy, slow dance.

A young, male attendant is giving a swimming-lesson. His pupil is a generously rounded woman wearing black goggles, her dark hair scraped into a neat dumpling on top of her head. With her plump, oval face and her topknot, and her eyes outlined in black, she reminds Rose of one of those women you see in old Japanese paintings, dispensing tea or holding lotus flowers and fans.

The woman hurls herself at the water and begins to plough furiously towards her instructor, her face screwed up with exertion, her arms chopping at the water in rapid arcs of panic. The attendant stands with his arms spread towards her, his fingers reaching to touch hers, urging her to swim that extra inch or two. But for all her wild efforts she is gradually sinking. When he sees she isn't going to make it he moves forward and grasps her hands.

The water lends everyone grace and innocence. The young pool attendant and the Japanese-looking woman would never touch in the real/unreal world outside. Here we are androgynous creatures, Rose thinks, dressed in virtually nothing, bumping each other, touching limbs as we pass in the water, sleek and bright in the warmth and the music, splashing about like amiable hippos.

A burst of sunlight gleams in through the far window and the ripples on the pool shimmer. Below the surface, the water is transformed to a phosphorescent green, like a glowing underwater cave. The tiles on the bottom of the pool are covered with shifting patterns, dancing threads of light. Rose swims closer. Each thread is a delicate, flickering rainbow under the water.

At the North Road Baths it was always cold. The fingers of cold pinched at your flesh. And he was always there, to watch as you shivered. I can help you improve your stroke, he would say. I can teach you to dive.

The attendant is tall, fair, lanky, with a gold earring. He chats to everyone, charming them with his white flash of a smile. He complimented Rose on her swimming. Rose was modest, protested that she was too slow. But it wasn't so much what he said, as the way he said it (he is Irish, southern Irish, with a soft lilt to his voice) and the way he smiled that made her go soft and wavery inside, like those rainbow threads of light under the water.

There was another man, once, who had made the rainbows flicker. David. His voice was low, kind, caressing. That was what Rose wanted; kindness, someone to hold her, warmth. Their bodies seemed to speak to each other, saying, save me, keep me from the cold. The sweetness of touch, just the two of you, in your own warm, soft world of light and sound, under the sea, swaying in the current, holding fast together.

I can teach you a lot. You'd be surprised how much I can teach you. And he would smile his awful smile. And the cold ran up and down your spine and the echoes screamed.

In front of Rose, a woman dives down to touch the bottom, sleek as a seal, in a swarm of tiny silvery bubbles. The rainbows flicker on the tiles. And Ms Serenity has arrived, slipping noiselessly into the water. Ms Serenity swims with a composed smile, her head elegantly poised. Her gleaming ash-blonde hair is carefully arranged on top of her head, where it stays miraculously dry, and she keeps her sparkly diamante spectacles perched on her nose.

Rose is not like that. Although she starts out looking neat and smooth in the pink swimsuit, her hair always ends up plastered in a soaking mass over her face, she gets cramp, her fingers go corrugated, her arms ache, her sinuses buzz and vibrate with the water pressure.

You never forget the echoes screaming and the bite of the cold.

Another gleam of sunlight lights up the pool and Rose plunges down. The phosphorescent cave is there, green and golden and glowing. She could swim into it, be surrounded by sparkling rainbow threads, swirled by warm currents, washed in soft music and moving harmonies of light. She remembers going to the beach with her mother, when she was little, before she could swim, before the North Road Baths. The water so blue and clear as she taught herself to float. The benign rocking of the sea beneath her and the lulling heat of the sun. She remembers the firm, corrugated sand under her toes, its ridges slightly painful to tender feet, yet exciting because it was all part of the childish ecstasy of being in the water.

The green glowing light is all around her now, the rainbows are shimmering and she has entered the phosphorescent cave. The music is soft and low, she is one of the rainbows, shimmering and sparkling, she is made of light and music. She is drawn further in, where the light grows brighter and softer and the rainbows dance and he is there, the attendant, the blond Irishman, like a merman in his cave, surrounded by light. He will save her from drowning. He stretches out his hands towards her, he almost touches her fingertips.

But then the cold sets in; the cold that is always there. The echoes screaming. Rose swallows water, breathes it in. She comes to the surface, coughing, the water burning in her lungs.

The echoes were so cold, you were white with cold, half dead with cold, the icy fingers pulling at you until you were made of ice.

The attendant is still holding out his hands to the Japanese-looking woman, who thrashes and chops at the shallow end. He gives her a square white polystyrene float. She stiffens herself like a board in the water, clinging to the float as a ship-wrecked person clings to a spar. The attendant smiles across at Rose. Briefly, the rainbows flicker.

After the first ecstatic plunge, the relationship with David had started to go wrong. He accused her of holding back from him. She wasn't giving herself fully enough, he said. The more she wanted him, the more he kept saying she was holding back.

Darling, darling David, how can I explain? That I was turned to ice, long, long ago at the North Road Baths. Like the little boy in the Hans Andersen story, kissed by the Snow Queen.

David lectured her about sex. You had to give yourself up to it, he said, or it didn't work.

I've tried to shut it out. But the echoes go on. Maybe I could tell you about it. Perhaps then they'd stop.

David told her she had a cold centre. He said she made him feel rejected.

If only you'd stay long enough to listen.

You need to learn to open up, David said.

My body flows to you and yearns for you. Each time, I think, this time it will be all right. But then I hear the echoes and I feel the cold, deep, deep inside. You have to turn yourself to ice, you see, as though it wasn't happening to you. As though the numb, goose-pimpled body in the swimsuit the green of brussels sprouts is someone else's body, not yours.

David usually gave his lecture as he was getting out of bed, as he always did immediately after they had had sex, or as he was scrubbing at his genitals in the bathroom. As he dashed out to his car, he would give her a quick kiss and say, Remember, you must learn to give yourself!

'That was nice, wasn't it?' he would say. And you had to say yes. Because he was a grown-up. Because he smiled and

smiled. You weren't allowed to be rude to grown-ups, especially when they smiled. So you said, yes it was nice. And it was so cold and the echoes would scream and scream like the mad gulls wheeling outside. And your body didn't feel like yours any more. It wasn't you it was happening to, it was somebody else.

After a while, David started to lose patience. He dug his nails in her back and he bit her, as if he thought that would help. At first, Rose submitted to this.

You have to pretend it's happening to somebody else.

Then, one day, Rose kicked him, quite hard. David said Ouch! very loudly. He sat up in bed and examined his shin with careful fingers. First you're frigid, he said, then you get violent. He climbed out of bed, cradling his wound. It's not so much the bruise, he said, you've really hurt my feelings. They didn't see each other again.

And the echoes scream on and on.

It's odd, Rose thinks, but if I'd been more like Ms Serenity, swimming so serene, head above water, David would probably have liked me better. But Rose can't just glitter on the surface and keep her hairdo dry.

You make it look effortless. That's what the attendant had said. You're a better swimmer than I am. And he had given her that smile and started the tiny rainbows shimmering.

She ploughs angrily up and down the pool, averting her head when she comes near the attendant, so as not to meet his eye. She swims harder and harder, trying to work away the little disturbing rainbows.

She leaves the pool and gets dressed. She leaves the phosphorescent green glowing cave and the threads of light shifting and flickering on the bottom of the pool. Ms Serenity still swims calmly up and down, her hair impeccably arranged, her spectacles glittering, scarcely disturbing the surface. The young attendant is holding out his hands to his pupil who still struggles and thrashes in the water, another inch, another, another, while he smiles and she strives to reach his fingertips, just before her in the water, only an inch away, just out of reach, always just out of reach. He glances at Rose as she goes, but she pretends not to see.

She leaves the Leisure Centre, its moist heat, its light, its echoey voices spreading, its palm tree with the imitation leaves. She shoves her way out through the swing doors, which close behind her with a gusty sigh. She plunges into the artificial real world outside, where a cold sun shines, where snow falls, where a real wind blows harsh and where people are bulked about with clothing, wrapped in layers of wool and nylon and polyester, and no-one sees who you really are inside.

Wayne Price

WHAT?

It was the day after the Everly Brothers played some big come-back concert in New York. We'd all been waiting for it. *Bye bye love,* Fran had gone on all the day before, *Bye bye happiness, hello emptiness, I feel like I could die-hi...* We'd all watched it on TV.

The next day we were looking at photos of our husbands. When the woman came in, white-faced and trying to be calm, Fran took them and slid them into the overdue books tray, giving her a nice helpful smile. The woman didn't smile back. Her eyes were snapped wide open like they'd been fixed like that.

My baby's gone, she said.

That was in the morning, about ten. She'd been our first customer that day; she came in with an overdue book, paid the fine and walked out. Now she was straight back in asking about this baby. None of us knew her.

We looked at each other, embarrassed, pursing up our lips, shaking our heads, that kind of thing.

I'll help you look, said Fran in the end. She kept her smile and it made the words seem nice and professional.

I've lost her, the woman said. She looked surprised, more than anything. Fran walked her to the door and out they went. Now where did you leave it, love? we heard Fran ask, and then the door clicked shut behind them.

Poor sod, whispered Jean to me. I'd die a thousand deaths. She shook her head at the closed door. I'd die, she said.

Fran and the woman were gone a whole hour. Jean and myself got on with things. We'd decided not to phone the police until the two of them got back, but as it turned out they brought the police back with them. The young lads in uniform followed them in and one asked us if we had a kettle handy.

Yes, I said kindly. Just in the back there. I pointed.

He made a face at me and twitched his head towards the woman who was crying by now, one arm folded tight across her middle, the other holding a knuckle up to her nose. Her head was down and she was shivering. She had nice thick auburn hair done in long loose curls and it fell down over her face. She'll be grateful for that, I thought. Then I said yes to the policeman again and walked around the desk to take the woman by the arm. Come on love, I said, or something, and I led her into the back room. This is where we have our tea-breaks, I told her nicely. I put the electric kettle on. What about some tea? I said.

She didn't answer. She still had her arm across her stomach and her face covered by all that nice hair. She was wearing these loose blue cotton trousers and a red pullover. There were red beads made into a butterfly pattern on it. I liked it. I made tea anyway. I put sugar in hers without asking. I thought even if she didn't want it she'd need the strength now.

When it was done she took it and started drinking, still not saying anything. Not even thankyou. Then she said, oh, sugar. But she went on sipping it anyway. Her voice was rough, like there was some loose stuff in her throat. It made me want to clear my own. Oh Christ, she said, and cried a bit more.

It was surprising to hear her speak like that. I smiled, in case she could see me, through all the hair. It seemed like a good time to start talking. It was awkward for me just sitting there. I thought for a bit and then I told her I'd given up sugar too. She looked at the cup in my hand, I think. It was hard to tell.

But I can drink it, I said. I like it. I just gave it up, that's all. For Weightwatchers, I said.

She let her head drop down so her hair was touching her legs. She sniffed and it made a big sucking noise.

All of us here go along, just for the company, I said, which was a lie, because Fran and Jean didn't go any more. But I did, and I wanted to get talking. You wouldn't know I went from looking at me, I said, I was born big, I said.

I don't know, she said. Which I didn't know how to answer.

We sat there quiet for a while. She was sitting right on the edge of her chair, still bent over, her nose nearly in her tea. Little bits of steam puffed up from the cup and against her forehead when she breathed.

I'm sure they'll find it, I told her.

Thankyou, she whispered.

Why don't you sit back? I said.

She did what I said. She let herself go back into the arm-chair. She sank down into it. It loosened the tension a little bit. I sat back too.

Do you want to phone home or anybody? I asked. Does your husband know yet? Do you want anyone to come?

She started up crying again. Her shoulders lifted away from the back of the chair, hunching right up. What am I going to tell him, she said. She cleared her throat, which I was glad about. Oh Jesus what's he going to say?

I didn't know what. I couldn't answer that at all. We both stayed quiet again.

Don't be afraid, I said after a while. I nodded. My husband George is a big man, I said. He's never hit me but sometimes he scares me, I said. You know?

I nearly went to get the photo out of the tray but in the end just moved to the side of her chair and put an arm round her.

You'll see, I told her, but I didn't know what she'd see. I squeezed her. I could feel her little bones through the pullover and I could smell her nice hair. I'll get you a tissue, I said.

At the counter Fran was stamping a cook book for some old man. It was a very fancy cookbook. In my job you meet all sorts.

How is she? Fran whispered.

You know, I said.

It'll work out, Fran said.

God help her if it doesn't, I said, and Fran looked at me, and I was surprised too.

I took the tissue box from under the counter and before going back looked in the tray for the photograph. While I'm here, I thought. I took the tissues and the picture in to her.

She was sitting on the edge of the chair again. I sat back on the arm of her chair and pulled out a tissue. She didn't try to take it from me, she just sat there like a kiddie, crying, her nose running. I put an arm round her again and put the tissue to her nose. It felt hot through the thin paper, then it went wet. I could feel my chest going, like a big strong machine. Blow, I said. Then I put it on the table and put the photo next to it. I took a fresh tissue and wiped around her eyes and over her cheeks. And it was then I felt something going, when I was wiping her face. I took her little head in between my hands and bent down to it. Maybe it's because she was so surprised she let me do it. Or maybe it's being frightened makes you let things happen. It tasted of salt and cigarettes and sweet tea. Mainly cigarettes. It was a shock. I hadn't seen her smoke and

I'd never tasted smoke on another mouth before. My husband has never smoked, though I used to secretly from time to time.

I stopped straight away. And that was just when Jean came in with the police anyway. The policeman took her out and left me to sit there, on my own. I bet she felt terrible. I bet she felt awkward as anything. I know I did. I'm not a young woman. By the time the door was pulled shut I was swimming. Like I was hollow and floating off. My insides, they didn't feel part of me. Lord, I was shaking.

That night, when I get home, George is in the bathroom. I shout to him, then get my coat off and get the cold potato out of the fridge and some sausages and eggs. I fry them all together. I put a lot of potato in, so much I need to keep adding more lumps of fat to stop it from sticking. George is a big man.

He comes out of the bedroom carrying an empty toilet paper tube. A little wisp of pink tissue trails off from it. I can't help noticing. He squashes it into the pedal bin. I turn the potato and roll the sausages. George sits down at the table and waits. I hand him a knife and fork and then roll the sausages again, making the fat spit. I stand there a while, and he sits there. One of the sausages splits right along its body with a crack and I look down. What's inside is this wet, human colour.

When it's all done I serve him: the potatoes first, then the sausages and then the eggs laid over the top of it all. I pass him the bottle of brown sauce from the cupboard and sit with him while he eats.

Not eating? he says.

No, I say.

He nods. You ought to stick at it, he says, and something falls back onto his plate.

George, I say.

What? he says.

You wouldn't believe what happened at work today.

No? he says. He looks at what it was that fell out of his mouth. He moves it to the edge of his plate with his fork. I don't want to look, but I'm looking.

No, I say. A woman lost her baby. A woman in the library, some woman I didn't know, and I had to look after her, in the tea-room.

He makes a noise and finishes what he's chewing.

Did they find it? he asks.

When he speaks I see a tiny puff of steam between his lips. It reminds me. Not that I need it. I don't know, I say.

I watch his food and the puffs of steam as he chews and cools it in his mouth. I wait and wonder if I'll ever be hungry again. For some reason, I want to go on talking. It seems suddenly like it's the opposite of eating. I wait and then,

George, I say.

What? he says

Elizabeth Simpson

THE NURSING HOME WEDDING

In trembling hands our glass of wine we held
Mild, I presume: not filled to the top
For at one hundred and twelve
We could hardly be expected to not spill a drop.

Many memories had foundered along the way
But not tastebuds with the recalled flavour of their yesterday
When legs could be expected to behave with honour
Trusted not to sag at the knee
Retain their pride to control the stride
When they'd been on the spree.

Oh come on, hurry up put your heids round that door
You said quarter past three
And it's now nearly four.

Inconsiderate Youth of eighty odd
You must be aware of how difficult our job
Waiting for you as well as God
To get his dates right so there'll be no backlog
To lengthen a queue, already long overdue.

The Wedding Cake's cut, awaiting the toasts
And so feels my throat, as we who can, sit here and gloat
Of our lesser infirmities.

Oh, here they are: the Bridal pair
Flushed with love or those five stair
A honeymoon in the Bahamas is out of reach
As is a cruise down the Nile to the Dam of Aswan
So they'll settle with relief in their familiar niche
Behind the Potted Palm.

Back to their cronies, the ultimate misnomer for hackneyed moaners
And a regular stroll down Memory Lane
We live cheek by jowl but can't remember their name
And if it wasn't for this pain
I'd complain
To have this yap of a chap removed from my domain.

We've lost our health, patience and strength
Gone the same way – our Pounds, Shillings and Pence
Plus all the time amidst this decline
Our waning sense
His, Hers, Yours and Mine.

Strangers all, hate pervades us
We cannot accept our dependent status
Unnatural: a dream
We must return to life's mainstream.

Ruth Thomas

OPTICAL ILLUSIONS

We have to wear our names on the front of our waitressing gear. Mine says 'Hello! My name is', then there is a gap. The supervisor, Mrs Crawford, biroed my name in the wrong place, so it slips just below the edge of the card. Adults are told never to let their children wear T-shirts with their names on them, in case creeping old men lure them into their Morris Minors. The same should apply to waitresses, particularly since 75% of the 'clientele' here are creeping old men.

My name is Rachel. Everyone here calls me Rache, and it's usually strung on the end of a waitressing sentence, like

'Table Two to go, Rache'

or

'Can you check we've got enough dessert spoons in the basket, Rache?'

I'm sitting beside the Cona coffee machine, reading a book called 'Fancy That!' It is full of optical illusions. There are pictures in it of creeping old men who also look like young girls, and rabbits that also look like squirrels. You can't see both images at once. The brain can't cope with the information at the same time. But it helps to pass the time.

This is my tea break. I am generously allowed twenty minutes, somewhere between six hours' waitressing, and only that because it's the law. The restaurant is a cross between an American Diner and Jo's Cafe. The spotty tables and plastic flowers are American, the bacon and eggs and greasy chips are British.

I've got to the end of my chapter, called 'Apparent Movement'. You're meant to stare at various shapes with lines in them, like spirals and grids, and the shapes are supposed to move or suddenly develop different colours. It's mildly interesting I suppose, but it doesn't seem to work with me. Or perhaps I've been here so long that things just look weird anyway.

'Does something appear to be running between the sets of lines?' the book queries, beneath a picture of six stripy rectangles. I think the answer must be 'Yes', otherwise the question wouldn't be there in the first place. But I can't see anything. Perhaps the corner I am in is too dark.

It is comforting though, like a simple text book. I am holding the stripy rectangle page under the light of the coffee machine when Mrs Crawford sweeps magnificently past.

'I think you've had long enough now, Rache,' she says. 'Time to give Cathy a break.'

She swivels her enormous boobs and the rest of her follows. She bellows into the kitchen, 'Cathy, 20 minutes.'

Then she creaks away in her pink managerial dress.

Almost instantly, the kitchen door swings open and Cathy runs to the staff table, rummaging for a packet of cigarettes in her pocket. She is the cook, responsible for getting the orders out on time. Her face is flushed and her mascara has run. The smell of frying onions in the kitchen is overwhelming. I can hear Billy, the kitchen assistant, re-tuning the radio from the local station to Radio One.

'What are you reading, Rache?' Cathy asks, frantically puffing a Marlborough.

I tell her it's called 'Fancy That!' The chapter I'm on is called 'Apparent Movement'.

'Sounds a bit like your waitressing.' She is a snide character. Sometimes I think I'd rather be alone with Mrs Crawford. At least Mrs Crawford is reliably tyrannical. She is, in fact, very much like a tyrannosaurus, lumbering violently through the small restaurant, clashing plates together, shrieking blood-curdlingly.

I put the book away to work on the cutlery basket. It is my job to make sure it is ready and glittering at all times. Each knife, fork and spoon set has to be wrapped up in a red paper napkin, and there is a separate section for long teaspoons – for eating ice cream and our speciality, eiderdown-thick milk shakes.

I am wrapping together some stray forks when a man taps me on the shoulder. 'This knife is dirty,' he says, clutching the offensive item. He is dirty too. His hands are grey and hairy and covered in oil. I am surprised by his high standards of knife cleanliness. But I don't say so. I just say,

'Would you like to select another knife then?'

Perhaps this sounds impolite. I don't know. But I see Mrs Crawford out of the corner of my eye, slinking round a corner and taking note.

'Thank you... Rachel,' says the man, leering ostentatiously

at my left breast. Then he trundles back to his ketchup-covered egg and chips. He is too basic to appreciate the little pot of heather I put on his table earlier, when the restaurant had been virtually empty.

Outside, the shopping mall is playing Handel's Water Music through the loudspeaker system so everyone thinks they are rich and having a good time. It is switched off abruptly and replaced by 'Simply Having A Wonderful Christmas Time'. The mall is open late for panicking Christmas shoppers, who are clicking quickly across the slippery floor into shop entrances. They don't look as if they are having a wonderful time, buying things for God-knows how many twice-removed cousins and neighbours they don't want to offend. Little bottles of geranium moisturising cream which look more expensive than they are. Autumn Bouquet pot pourri mixtures. In shop windows there are signs saying EVERYTHING REDUCED. Tiny handbags and fairy shoes.

There are several people sitting round the phone kiosk. It is a low, moulded plastic contraption with four 'booths' at each corner. A Chinese girl, in a red raincoat, looks bored as she waits for one of the booths to empty.

When I turn to face the restaurant again, I am aware of some sort of commotion going on at Cathy's table. She looks hot and angry, and she is talking aggressively to Mrs Crawford, who stands with her hands on her hips.

My vision has little glowing telephones booths in it. I've been staring at them too long, and now they impose themselves upon the two gesticulating women. They float downwards, from chair level to the floor, and when I blink, they start all over again. Little telephone ghosts. They hover for ages.

Cathy is embarrassingly loud. Some of the depressed eaters raise their heads from their food troughs and look for the noise. At the most remote table in the room, next to the Ladies and Gents, a middle-aged couple look lost and lonely. They ignore Cathy's raised voice and continue with their grilled tomatoes, chewing slowly, their eyes fixed on invisible things. Scattered underneath the table are bags containing wrapping paper and cellophane boxes.

I collect a few plates from tables, pretending the scene in the corner does not exist. The plates are grim, bits of egg yolk and Daddy's Sauce smeared round the edges. I never get used to it. At one table, a woman drinking coffee asks me if I know what's going on.

'I think it must be the stress of Christmas,' I say, smiling like a martyr and sweeping a few raisins onto her lap with a damp cloth.

As I swing into the kitchen Mrs Crawford is hissing like a piece of bacon under the grill. She looks angrily around the restaurant with bulging eyes.

'Look Cathy, I just didn't realise how many customers we'd get this evening. I'm asking you to do one extra hour. I'll pay you overtime.'

'Well that's just too bad,' says Cathy, 'because my boyfriend is coming to pick me up in 5 minutes and there's no way I'm staying just because you didn't plan ahead properly.'

The argument makes me feel cold and I dive into the kitchen, stacking the plates into the big silver dishwasher and shoving the rack through.

When I go out into the restaurant again, Cathy is taking her apron off. She chucks it into the laundry basket by the coat rack, then pulls her jacket off a peg.

'That's it, then Rache,' she says, 'I'm off.'

She is triumphant but her voice is shaking. She sweeps grandly out of the restaurant door, upright, with watery eyes. She doesn't say goodbye. This is the last I will see of her.

Mrs Crawford is talking to herself, and swearing, polishing plant leaves in a frenzy at the till. She is almost frightening. When I walk past she grabs me and pushes me, as if I'm a vacuum cleaner, through the kitchen door. We are face to face by the frying pans.

'No doubt you heard that little episode Rachel,' she says, folding her chins into the top of her apron. Her face is angular and dented as a cheese grater, behind a pair of pink-rimmed glasses. Sometimes, when she looms her jowls at me, I stop listening and just watch the strain in her eyes. Behind the pink, they are green and desperate.

'You'll have to help in the kitchen,' she's saying. 'Have you done much cooking for large numbers?'

So I find myself at the draining board, learning how to cook for large numbers, chopping up onions and peeling potatoes. Billy has been promoted to head cook. He stands at the huge, hot hob, shuffling an oily pan of eggs around.

'So Cathy got the sack then, eh?' he asks me, giving the vat of baked beans a quick stir with the egg spatula.

'Looks like it.'

I am wary of Billy. It is likely he will slap my bum if we stand together at the cooker. He is singing to a tune on the radio, and suddenly stops to say,

'I'm leaving as well.'

It seems Christmas is the time for escape.

'Don't leave me Billy.' I'm genuinely pleading, fluttering my eyelashes and getting to grips with a large onion. 'Don't leave me to the mercy of Mrs Crawford.'

The radio on the shelf is covered in grease. Somehow a voice manages to emerge through it.

'Now, here's one of my favourites,' says the presenter, revelling in his jolliness. 'Frosty the Snowman.'

'What is this?' asks Billy and snatches the dial onto another channel. He tunes into the end of 'So here it is, Merry Christmas, everybody's having fun...'

The onions are horrendously strong, the big, bright Spanish kind which turn into little rivers when you cut them. I brush my eyes with the edge of my cuff but it just makes them sting even more.

'Strong, aren't they?' says Billy, 'It's much better if you cut them under running water.'

'I've heard you're meant to put a knife between your teeth.'

'Well that's just asking for trouble, isn't it?'

And then he gives me a quick slap.

He's about four years younger than me, and about ten years more arrogant.

'I'm going to be sous-chef at the Argyle Hotel in January,' he tells me. 'I might be able to smuggle you some free dinners there if you play your cards right.' He hums back to the baked beans.

I turn on the tap. The water is freezing but it takes away the sting of the onions. I can see again.

Billy switches on the air extractor. It's as hot and smoky as Hell in here. There are no windows, just a circle in the swing door, which looks out into the restaurant. Through the circle, I can see Mrs Crawford, like a large goldfish collecting plates. Her thin chignon is falling out. Not one of the customers talks to her. The floor vibrates when she stomps across it. I see her advancing towards the door and leg it back to the onions.

'Table Four want two Christmas Bucks Fizz Sundaes,' she says, flatly, over her shoulder, then launches herself through the door again. It makes a squashy noise as it flaps back into place.

'Can you do those?' asks Billy. He explains. Two scoops of vanilla ice cream, a splodge of chocolate sauce and some black cherry sauce. Then squirt cream over them.

'And they need some sparklers.'

He emerges from the store cupboard, waving some metal sticks at me.

'Are you sure?' I say. It's not Mrs Crawford's style.

'It's Christmas, isn't it? That's why they're called Christmas Buck's Fizz. Anyway, this is my last day here. I can do what I want.'

I walk flat-footedly across the broken floor to the freezer. Inside there are dozens of half-empty boxes of ice cream. They squeak painfully as I turn them over, looking for the vanilla. Eventually I find it, wedged between a Genuine Austrian Strudel and an Arctic Roll.

The chocolate and cherry sauces are waiting on the hob. I pour both over the ice cream and watch it all melt together. It looks like the little tubes you can buy at the beach, containing layers of coloured sand.

'Is that OK?' I ask Billy

"Nice one,' he says, and advances on them with a large container of pressurised cream, squirting a large, white bee-hive on each.

We stick six sparklers into the cream and light them with a Cook's Match. They spit at us innocently. Tiny little yellow sparks.

'Go on, then, before they go out.'

Billy shoves me through the door. I've still got my oniony apron on. I get a couple of ice cream spoons from the basket, ignoring wisecracks from the dirty knife man.

Table Four is the lonely middle-aged couple by the toilets. I arrive at their table, feeling like a firework display.

'Sparklers!' says the woman.

Amazing what a bit of fire can do. It's actually caused a Christmas mood in this crummy place. A couple of fat businessmen have got paper hats from somewhere, about the same purple as their faces. And a group of girls, celebrating their last day at work, are screaming and shrieking with red

Christmas tree baubles dangling from their ears.

I go round the tables collecting empty plates and glasses with redundant straws in them.

When I push through to the kitchen again, a tray of eggy plates in my hands, Mrs Crawford is in there, reprimanding Billy for the sparklers. He is just standing there, with his hands behind his back.

'I am the one who decides when to put sparklers in the ice cream,' she is saying. Her pink dress has a blob of squirty cream on the front. A black hair-grip hangs by a fine, pale hair, and bangs against the side of her ear. Billy has propped my book up behind the spatulas, and it looks as if it is just about to slide forward and fall on her head. He's got it open at the chapter called 'Can You Believe Your Eyes?'.

'I am the manager here.' She is huge and pink, like a big Christmas tree fairy. 'So no more smart ideas, OK, Billy, even if it is what they call the Festive Season.'

Something about her flopping hair, her sarcasm, makes me smile. Billy is silent. From behind his back, he produces another Christmas Bucks Fizz Sundae. It's kind of rudely extravagant, with five sparklers poked into the cream. He puts the glass down by the hob and lights the sparklers.

'For you,' he says.

Then he pulls my book out from behind the spatulas, and takes it with him back to the deep fat fryer.

Mrs Crawford and I stare at the yellow flecks for a minute. She has gone very quiet, as if she has been deflated like a bicycle tyre. She breathes peacefully through her nose. I turn away and there are little blue images, like fireflies, dancing behind my eyes. When I look back again, Mrs Crawford has unwrapped a dessert spoon from its red napkin and is licking a tiny piece of cream off the end of it. Her face looks different. There appears to be something running slowly behind her glasses.

'I'm sorry,' she's saying, 'I'm sorry.'

Valerie Thornton

ABOUT NOT SMOKING

I've taken to standing in doorways. In the doorway between the kitchen and the hall mostly. Maybe because it's the safest place when the ground is shifting under your feet. As opposed to the earth moving, that is.

Sometimes with a cigarette. Sometimes not. I don't smoke. I give up after every packet. All the time.

Sometimes in the dark. Always in one kind of dark, sometimes two.

I've also taken to watching lives from a little distance. Watching other people live. It's something I don't really do now. Living.

Strawberries are good for stubbing cigarettes out on. A satisfying hiss and no gunge to prise off the ashtray with a finger nail, which then needs the gunge prised out of it too.

White on red. Hissing. I only smoke all-white cigarettes. If I smoke. They're purer. Surely. With green stars above the filter. I like green. And stars. Nine on each cigarette. Nine on each strawberried stub.

Why not ten? There's ten in the packet. I only buy tens because I don't smoke.

If it's dark, I'm not in. Therefore it's not me smoking either.

The pure white logic of it makes me light-headed and the ground still shifts under my feet.

Gael Turnbull

THE REAL NEWS

'Bald limestone in early spring,
now much greener. Rain almost every day.
Ireland set to dissolve. Grey skies.
All the more reason to hug the bright ones.
What is it about Africa, I can't shake off?
Two years now since I've seen someone casually
dance down a street. How are you? Here's
raw from last evening: a gorgeous moth,
black and red, finest and strangest ever.

Sometimes just want to shout: Thanks. Or
the camomile tea has gone to my head? Paradise:
a small livelihood, all my books in order
together in a house, absence of relatives,
an open notebook. While this place: turning
into a blue cheese, starting in bathroom
and working out. But looking back or forward,
it's a bad habit. Stop. Here's my son
with the real news. *Dinner's ready.*'

Fred Urquhart

FORTY THREE YEARS: A BENEDICTION

I met Peter Wyndham Allen on 25th May 1947. We fell in love, and we lived together for forty-three years until he died, aged eighty-two, on 9th November 1990. It was a very happy homosexual marriage.

The 25th May was a beautiful sunny early summer day. I was living then in a chalet at Bellingdon near Chesham, Bucks. In the morning I went to London by train for a lunch appointment. I wore a very smart green tweed suit that a former lover, Dr Nigel Monro, had forced me to have made at his tailor's. It was very expensive, and, although I'm naturally quite extravagant, I resented the price and, as a result, was not very fond of the suit. Nigel, the son of Harold Monro, the poet, had been my first lover when I was twenty-two and he was a medical student in Edinburgh. He had reappeared in my life in London in 1946, and I learned that he was now married and had two children. He intended to divorce his wife, so he had wanted me to accompany him to Rouen and keep him company until the divorce. He was keen to start our affair again, but I was suspicious. Nigel took drugs; he was very temperamental; and I did not fancy being implicated in a divorce. So I'd parted with him just before Christmas, 1946. After a row, I left him at the door of the Café Royal, and he shouted venomously after me, 'Good night, dear queen.'

I was going to have lunch with my friend José Wilson, fiction editor of *Woman's Own*. The editor, James Wedgwood Drawbell, was a fellow Scot and he'd encouraged me to write some romantic stories which were a little bit different from my usual realistic ones. He paid me fifty pounds a story, a high price in those days, so with tongue in cheek I did the best I could. Miss Wilson, an iconoclast like myself, and I had many a laugh at the results. We laughed especially at *The Last G.I. Bride Wore Tartan*, which I wrote at the time, although I knew perfectly well it was unsuitable as well as too long for *Woman's Own*; it would have filled two issues of the paper. When eventually it was published as the title story in a collection, I dedicated the book to José. She was great fun, and we often went pub-crawling together. One evening in December

1946 we went with Peter Davies, brother of Rhys Davies, the great Welsh short story writer, with whom I was sharing a flat in Holborn, to what would now be called a gay pub in Stepney.

It was packed with well-known London characters as well as sailors and soldiers. At closing time we needed to pee, so José went to seek a Ladies and Peter and I went into the Gents. I was standing next to a very tall handsome sailor, covertly and covetously eyeing what he possessed, when Miss Wilson swept in and went into the WC. The sailor grinned at me and said: 'Oh, miss, you're no lady.' I grinned back and said she was a lady and a very nice one and that pubs should provide facilities for women drinkers. We got on the chat, and as we did ourselves up I knew I'd clicked. He had a pal with him, another sailor not quite as good looking but very personable. They came back with José and Peter and me to Princeton Street, where we produced more drinks. Eventually José went home to Baker Street in a taxi, but the sailors stayed on. I slept with the handsome one, whose name was Fred (I still remember his surname, but will keep it to myself). I had the best one-night-stand I've ever had. Although Fred would not let me kiss him on the mouth he let me kiss him everywhere else I fancied. I've often thought about him in the past 45 years and I've had the pleasure of a remembering rise every time. Next morning Fred and his friend said they were going to a wedding in Hackney. It was just after they'd gone that I realised the wedding was Fred's own.

After lunch José went back to her office, so I went to the Wheatsheaf in Rathbone Place, just off Oxford Street, to see what I could pick up. The pub, one of the most popular in Soho, was empty, for it was getting on for closing time. I talked with Red, the publican, and his wife Frances, wondering what to do; I didn't feel like returning to Bellingdon so early in the day.

The swing doors burst open and in breezed Miss Nina Hamnett, the Queen of Soho, followed by a tall blonde young man. Nina and I greeted each other effusively, and she introduced the good looking man as Peter Wyndham Allen. She was surprised we didn't already know each other. I had known Nina since 1944, but Peter had known her for many years before that, and he was a regular visitor to the Wheatsheaf and other Fiztrovia and Soho pubs. Peter was taller than me:

about six feet. We took to each other at once. It turned out that 25th May was his birthday. He was thirty-nine, four years older than me. Nina did not divulge her age. She was already well advanced in years after a very gay and busy life as an artist in Paris and London. She had sat as a model for Modigliani, who had once chased her up a lamp-post. In 1932 she'd published her autobiography *Laughing Torso*, a sensational book at the time and still well worth reading for the picture she gives of bohemian life in Paris in the early 1920s.

When Red reluctantly closed the Wheatsheaf at three o'clock, Nina and Peter and me took a taxi to Anne's Club, which was in an alley just off Fleet Street. We drank a lot in the next few hours, then we went back to the Soho pubs. We lost Miss Hamnett in one of them. She just disappeared, as she often did when she decided she'd had enough to drink. About ten o'clock Peter and I got on the train for Chesham. We had an empty carriage in a non-corridor train, so we were able to make love. We were intoxicated with each other, as well as drink, when we reached Chesham. The last bus had gone, so we walked to Bellingdon. I knew a short cut through the fields. It was a full moon, a beautiful night, and we were idyllically happy as we walked along hand in hand beside the hedges, stopping every now and then to cuddle and kiss.

Peter was Irish. When he was a boy the family stayed a lot at Ardmore in County Waterford, and there he was taught his first steps in sex by another boy, Teddy, who had green eyes and greenish-gold hair. They used to dance together, and once they did an exhibition foxtrot for a Mother Superior, who was enchanted. They became friends with a middle-aged sailor who lived in a cottage at Whiting Bay, along the shore from Ardmore. They visited him frequently and secretly, and he taught them a great deal more about sex. The inhabitants of Ardmore thought the sailor was interested in girls, and virgin types were forbidden to go near his cottage. The folk of Ardmore were quite mistaken; Peter and Teddy could have opened their eyes. Even in his old age Peter used to get quite lyrical and nostalgic about the sailor. Peter said I reminded him of Teddy, for I have green eyes and when we first met my hair was greenish-gold and it remained that colour even when it began to thin.

Peter's real name was Patric Grant-Forde. He changed it to his grandmother's name when he went on the stage. His paternal grandmother had been a Wyndham Quin, and she was a granddaughter of an Earl of Dunraven. After her first husband died, she married a Mr Allen of Crosseley in Wales and called herself Wyndham Allen. Peter's father, Patric Grant-Forde, was a captain in the Irish Guards, and he was commanding a Ghurka regiment when he was killed early in the 1914–1918 War. His mother, Olivia Montgomery-Moore, belonged to another old Irish family. Olivia's mother died when she was very young and she was brought up by her aunt, Miss Angelina Boyce, who acted as hostess to her sister's widower, Aitchison Montgomery-Moore, a diplomat in Russia and other countries. Angelina also brought up Peter after his father's death, for Olivia was still very young and susceptible to men, and she had several affairs that shocked her aristocratic relatives and enraged Angelina.

Peter was educated at a prep school run by Jesuits near St Albans, then he went to Marlborough. In his teens, mad about dancing, he joined Marie Rambert's Ballet Company. There was another Grant in the company, so Peter changed his name to Wyndham Allen, and Wyndham Allen he remained for the rest of his life. After the Ballet Rambert he went to the Sadlers Wells Ballet, and in the early 1920s went with the company to New York. Oddly enough, considering his propensities, he did not like young American men, and he always spoke slightingly of those he met socially in New York and Long Island. He was with the Sadlers Wells when the fifteen-year-old Margot Fonteyn joined it, and he often used to tell stories of the tomboyish Margot and her penchant for the Charleston and other philistine ballroom dancing. He left the Sadlers Wells; Ninette de Valois always said that he didn't concentrate enough. He found the severe ballet training irksome, and he could not be bothered spending four or five hours at the bar. I suppose he preferred, like myself, to lean against another kind of bar with a glass in his hand. Then he joined the Ballet Russe de Monte Carlo, but he fell off the stage and damaged his right leg so badly that it was the end of his ballet career. He considered teaching ballroom dancing, but nothing came of that. He drifted from one job to another. Once as a sports master in a boarding school. He was very athletic; he swam all the year round when he was young, and he was a good tennis player. He stayed for longish periods at a time in North Wales with Aunt Angelina when she wasn't making trips to Florence,

France and Ireland, and he stayed occasionally with Olivia and her fourth husband, Laurence Furze, a South African whom Peter disliked. Then through a woman friend in the film world he got a job on the technical side in Warner Brothers' London Office in Wardour Street. He was there until shortly before World War Two started.

He was working as a companion-help and social secretary for a stockbroker and his wife in Weybridge when I met him. Part of his job seemed to be keeping the wife company in the local pubs. The couple were moving to the Scilly Isles, but Peter didn't want to go with them. So, a few weeks after we met, he came to Bellingdon to live with me. We were never parted after that.

We moved to London that autumn when I took a job in a literary agency. We lived in Islington and Notting Hill Gate before we moved to the top flat at number one Bloomsbury Street, where we stayed for about three years. This flat had belonged to Michael Joseph, the publisher, when he was married to Hermione Gingold. It was carpeted in navy blue and was all white paint. We loved it until we discovered that rats were invading it. The back was directly opposite the back of the Ivanhoe Hotel's kitchens, so the rats could approach along the parapets where Michael Joseph and his wife used to let out their cats. We got the Holborn rat-catcher to get rid of the rats but not before one got under the divan in the sittingroom and I tried foolishly to poke it out with the poker and Peter sitting in his bath saw one appearing through the window on top of the cistern. After that we put wired frames on the windows to keep them from returning.

Some of my friends criticised Peter for not getting a job, but he had a full-time job looking after me. He did the cooking, the housework and the shopping; and I didn't need to do anything in the house except wash an occasional dish. We were very happy with this arrangement. While we lived in London he had a number of temporary jobs that satisfied the criticism of our friends. He worked sometimes for Book Tokens and looked after their stall at several *Sunday Times* exhibitions in Grosvenor House; he had a job as a salesman at a book exhibition in Olympia; and he worked for a time as an agent in a census. These short-lived jobs helped enormously, for we were often hard up and waiting payment for short stories and book reviews. Though we never let our hardupness worry us too much; we learned to grin and bear it. I brazenly borrowed cash or wrote post-dated cheques.

In Bloomsbury Street we were near the Soho pubs, so we spent a good deal of time in the Wheatsheaf, the Fitzroy, the French pub, the Caves de France and the Mandrake where we drank with Nina Hamnett, Sylvia Gough, Nina's rival for the queenship of Soho, Robert MacBryde and Robert Colquhoun and John Minton, the artists, all old friends of mine, as well as Vernon Scannell, Dylan Thomas, Julian Maclaren Ross, Rhys Davies, the young Jeffrey Bernard, who was only fifteen when we first met him, and many other well-known Soho characters. A malicious friend of the Roberts christened us 'the Royal Family', but we didn't give a bugger; we didn't look like queens except maybe to some of the initiated. Once, as I was coming out of the lavatory in The Highlander, a man going in said: 'You look like an old cow.' I was furious, but it turned out that what he'd said was: 'You look like Noel Coward.'

I always laugh at that, especially when, tired of the hectic London life, we moved to the country and stayed for a winter in a cottage at Aldington, close to the Romney Marsh in Kent, and Noel Coward lived about a couple of hundred yards along the road at Goldencrest Farm. We met face to face once in Ashford Station, but otherwise I never knew him.

We sampled several other country cottages before, on 4th April 1958, we went to Spring Garden Cottage, an isolated dwelling in the middle of the Ashdown Forest. It was found for us by my friend John Pudney, who lived at Cherry Orchard, a house on the other side of Fairwarp, the village nearest to Spring Garden. We never thought when we moved in that lovely April day that we'd live here for the next thirty-two years.

Spring Garden belonged to Gwenda Downes, an old lady who lived with her sister Joan in another cottage about a mile away. We rented it for three guineas a week. It was not long before Gwenda and Peter discovered that they were distant cousins, and it was not long before Gwenda, who was about eighty at the time, fell in love with Peter, whom she always spoke of to me as 'Our handsome Irish gentleman'. That was a great help when occasionally we could not pay the rent on the dot! I became very friendly with Joan Downes, who, like me, was almost a chain-smoker. After we'd been here for two or three years Joan became ill with cancer of the throat. The first time I visited her in Guy's Hospital in London, her first words were: 'Have you brought any fags?' Poor Joan, she came home half the woman she'd been, and she died soon after. She was seventy-two. Gwenda, ten years older, wasn't able to look after herself, although she had a daily help; so Peter visited her every afternoon and stayed until early evening, cooking her supper and talking and listening to her stories of her past when she was a governess in Switzerland and wrote religious plays. One of them was produced and had the young Flora Robson in the cast.

For the next ten years Peter divided his time between looking after Gwenda and looking after me and Spring Garden Cottage. He had tremendous energy, far more than I ever had. He worked in the garden, growing a variety of vegetables as well as many flowers in beds between a good deal of grass, which he cut regularly with great determination. He cooked all our meals, and he did most of the housework. I did a little housework between periods of sitting at the typewriter, but I never did any cooking. The only thing I could cook was scrambled eggs. So, since Peter died, I've had to learn, and now I can do a passable cauliflower cheese. But I get irritated at all the time spent in preparing something that's eaten in a few minutes.

Even before we left London Peter started giving me breakfast in bed. He always got up early; he didn't like lying in bed but knew I did. So he said it was better for me to lie still and read or write. For almost all those forty-three years, therefore, I lay in bed most mornings until ten o'clock. I read MSS for publishers and review books, and I wrote little bits of stories and novels, so I was always able to say I was working when some people made rude remarks about my late rising. I never felt guilty. I never feel guilty about anything.

Occasionally Peter and I had extramarital affairs, but these were never serious and we always told each other about them. Sometimes we shared the same lover and slept three in a bed. We did that with one of mine called Derek. He was a guardsman, a very good looking lively young man with the biggest phallus I've ever seen, about a foot long in repose. He picked me up in the Mandrake Club one Saturday afternoon. I don't know how it happened, for I wasn't aware of him until he suddenly appeared at my side and began talking. Afterwards I guessed that somebody must have pointed me out as a fairly promiscuous and well-known sexual adventurer and easy pickings for cash. Derek pretended he was a writer and told me he'd written a book just published. I'd never read this book, but I'd read the reviews, and so had Derek. Anyway, he stayed with us in Bloomsbury Street for a week, and we went drinking every night. Women, oddly enough, didn't take to him; not any of our female friends, anyway, like Elisabeth Smart and Elyse Livingstone, to whom we introduced him. Even Nina Hamnett, who liked handsome young men, was sniffy. They must have suspected that he was abnormally large sexually. At the end of the week he 'borrowed' a pound to go to Pirbright. We never saw him again. When he didn't come back I began to suspect that he was a deserter and that he'd gone to Pirbright to give himself up. I've often thought about him over the years, wondering what happened, for I'd grown fond of him in that week of sex and drink. He was an unhappy mixed up boy, and the army was the wrong place for him.

Peter had an affair with John Deakin, the photographer. John was a friend of both of us, but Peter saw him oftener than I did. They had their affair in the early 'sixties when I was working for Walt Disney and had to go to London twice a week as his 'scout'. Peter always went with me and visited Olivia, who was in a poor state of health and living in Chelsea. In the afternoons he returned to the West End and went to Soho, and he always seemed to be running into John Deakin. John often talked about photographing me, but we were never able to have an opportunity, and I regret it now. The truth is that we were always so busy drinking that we got pissed, and Peter and I had usually to catch the last train to Tunbridge Wells, or we stayed the night with Anthony and Therese Cronin and photography was out of the question. This was all brought back to me last week when I watched a television programme about John Deakin and his work. I wish Peter could have seen it. We knew almost everybody who appeared in it – Francis Bacon, Daniel Farson, Johnny Minton and the Roberts, Muriel Belcher who ran the Colony Room Club, and an old white haired man who turned out to be the now famous Jeff Bernard whose bum I'd often pinched when he was young. He had always said: 'That'll cost you five bob, Fred.' I kept turning to Peter to say 'Look at him!' or 'Listen to that!' but of course he wasn't there. They are all dead now except Francis Bacon, Danny Farson, the Bernard brothers and me, and by the end of the programme I was in tears.

Gwenda died, aged ninety, in 1975. She was going to leave some money and Spring Garden Cottage to Peter, but he insisted that the cottage should also be left to me, for I'd also done a lot of work for her, typing and retyping her huge correspondence. So when she died we inherited the cottage between us, and so for the past sixteen years we've been responsible for it, and have been very happy even when we didn't have the money to do any necessary repairs, although we should, I suppose, have taken some out of our building society accounts.

Peter was still active when he reached the age of eighty. Then he began to speak about death. His mother and his Aunt Angelina had been seventy-eight when they died. He said that none of his family lived any longer than that. I reminded him that his mother's granny had lived until she was eighty-three and many bottles were found under the floor-boards in her room; she had been helped by a faithful old maid to enjoy herself to the last minute. But Peter couldn't remember that story he'd told me at various times over the years. He was becoming forgetful. And by the time he reached eighty-one he was losing his memory in a distressing way. He was no longer able to work in the garden, so we got Peter Lushington, a delightful well-educated good looking young man, whom we christened Young Pete, to come two or three times a week to cut the grass, saw logs and do other jobs too heavy for us. Young Pete soon became one of the family, and both Peter and I fell in love with him when we saw him, wearing only the briefest of shorts, cutting the grass in the hot summer sunshine. He was like a beautiful young faun.

Peter – now Old Pete – still went for his daily walk, but the walks were getting shorter and he had to give up his favourite one of about five miles towards Nutley Windmill and Old Lodge because it was very hilly.

When Peter was eighty the doctor diagnosed that I had diabetes, so I had to start taking eight pills a day. And then I had a slight stroke which made my hands even more inefficient than ever. I've always been awkward or pawly with my hands, except when writing, drawing, sewing or typing; and when I was young my father or brothers always took the hammer away from me if I tried to drive in a nail. I'd never worried about it, however, until I had the stroke. An X-ray revealed that I had a damaged spine, the result of falling off a horse when I was twenty-two. The doctor wanted me to wear one of those high stiff white collars, but I refused; I said I'd rather put up with the numbness in my hands and wrists.

Just before his eighty-second birthday Peter developed acute sciatica. The doctor could do nothing for it except give him pain killers; but seeing that we were having a difficult time he got in touch with the welfare people and they gave us our dear Emmi Deeprose as a home help. Since then, Emmi, an Austrian who came to England when she was fifteen and became a psychiatric nurse, has visited us once a week and cheered us up as well as doing the hard core of housework.

On one of his visits the doctor told me that Peter's heart was beating too quickly. He gave him lanoxin tablets, two a day, which Peter would never have remembered to take if I hadn't given them to him morning and lunchtime. He always asked what they were and why he had to take them, but I managed to be evasive and never told him why.

In the six months after his eighty-second birthday Peter got frailer and frailer, though he still went for his walks and never became bedridden. I made him stay in bed in the mornings until I'd given him breakfast, but he always kicked up a fuss and said he'd prefer to get up. At the beginning of November he complained of pains in the chest, and he had difficulty in breathing, but he refused to have the doctor and still went for short walks. Behind his back, however, encouraged by Emmi, I phoned the surgery. Our own doctor was on a short holiday, but another one came and said that Peter had a chest infection, and he gave him antibiotics. Peter had been losing his appetite, but he began to regain it after taking the antibiotics, and on the Thursday, after being out walking for about an hour (very slowly and standing about a lot talking to women he knew on horses) he said he'd enjoyed his lunch. He also ate a good supper, and afterwards we watched television. I noticed, though, that he coughed a good deal through the night.

Next morning, Friday 9th November, when I got up at half past seven and was drawing the curtains, he said: 'If this cold weather continues it'll be the end of me. I'll have to go into hospital.'

These were the last words he spoke. Half an hour later when I took him a cup of hot water and glauber salts, which he had every morning, he was sitting up in bed with his eyes closed, blowing out his cheeks and making a funny noise. I said: 'What's wrong?' He never answered. He went on blowing for a few seconds and then stopped. He was dead.

I couldn't believe it. At first I thought he was playing a trick. And then I realised what it was. It was a great shock, for I'd expected him to live for another year or two. I phoned the doctor, but the surgery wasn't open yet; I got an answerphone woman with an awful voice who kept saying: 'If in trouble phone Buxted' and a number that was unintelligible. I tried two or three times to see if I could get it clearly, but couldn't; so I phoned our friend and nearest neighbour, Cathy Hayes, and she came down in five minutes and it was she who phoned the doctor and then the undertaker.

His body, covered by a blanket, was carried out on a stretcher to the hearse just over an hour afterwards. The grass on the Forest was slippy, the driver could not get the hearse to move, so we had to get old carpets to put under the wheels before they got away. How Peter would have laughed at such a departure.

He was cremated in Tunbridge Wells on Thursday 16th November. Although he belonged to Irish Protestant families, Peter had become a Roman Catholic when he was twelve. His mother had fallen in love with a priest, and she made Peter turn Catholic with her. He was a non-practising Catholic, however, and never went to any church, except to friends' funerals, in all the years I lived with him. But I had a Catholic service for him. There were twenty-two friends at the cremation, including five good-looking young men, which would have pleased him. After the service, at the going-away party which Cathy and Arthur Hayes gave, the priest, Father Morris, told me that one of the young men had been crying. I think I know which one, although I was sitting in the front pew between Cathy and Emmi, looking only at the coffin and trying desperately not to burst out crying myself.

Five months after the cremation, I got Peter's ashes in a casket. One evening Young Pete took me in his car to Peter's favourite walk across the Forest, and I scattered his ashes in the bracken beside it, as I'd promised him.

I am now in the process of trying to sell Spring Garden Cottage. I've had a miserable winter here on my own and I can't cope any longer. I've lived here for thirty-three years and

I love the place, but I just can't live alone. I've been in England for forty-seven years. It's time I went home. I'm going back to Edinburgh where I hope to get a flat near my brother Morris. Five years ago Peter and I decided we'd sell the cottage and retire to Edinburgh. He loved Edinburgh, and we realised then we were too old to run this place much longer. But we were never able to get around to doing anything, and soon we knew that Peter would never be able to make the move.

As long as I remain here he'll never be dead. For years we have shopped in Uckfield, going every Wednesday with our friend Arthur Hayes in his Daimler. Every Wednesday morning we have phoned the bread shop and ordered six soft brown rolls and two uncut Hovis loaves. We used the name Allan because it is much simpler than Urquhart. So every week when I still phone and ask for one Hovis and the rolls the girl says: 'Righto, Mr Allan, I'll put them by for you.' So Mr Allan gets his bread although the real Mr Allan had not been in the shop for well over a year.

I'll be sorry to leave the Ashdown Forest with all its happy memories, but I'll carry our handsome Irish gentleman back to Scotland in my heart.

Billy Watt

FISH

It was morning break. By the sud-fringed burn
that skittered from the annexe to boys' cludge
someone had found a trout, dead, on the grass.

Some speculative tosses, boys to girls,
soon soared into a lobbing competition
between their netball stands and our goalposts.

Soon we were all in it: a gathering
matched only by each term's keelhaul to church,
a playground strike in the gallus sixties ...

I watched its slack weight arching overhead,
scunnered and yet, yes, ducking with the rest:
mad squeals beneath disintegrating flesh.

It landed at my feet once: flecked with red,
its soft scales shredded, and a ganting mouth
turned down to all that life could chuck at it.

Then it was whirled away again, flipped higher
than those hills that spat it out. Down from
Loch Thom, the Cut, the Horsetail waterfall,

that trout had spermed its way to our playground –
and it's taken me till now to see myself
there, fish out of water, on searing tar.

Irvine Welsh

SPORT FOR ALL

See that big skinny gadge wi the tartan skerf? Big Adam's Aypil hingin ower the toap ay it? Ah'm jist gaunny huv a wee word wi the cunt.

Whit d'yis mean leave um? Ah'm jist wantin a wee bit ay a spraff wi the boy, aboot the game n that eh.

Hi mate, been tae the rugby? Murrayfield, aye? Scotlin win aye?

Fuckin sound.

Hear that Skanko? Scotlin fuckin won.

Whae wis it thi wir playin mate? Fiji. FIJI!? Who the fuck's that?!

FIJI! Some fuckin islands ya doss cunt.

Aye?

Aye, we'll we're jist some fuckin islands tae these cunts, think aboot it that wey.

It's right enough though, eh mate?

Still, wir aw fuckin Scotsmin the gither, eh mate?

No thit ah ken much aboot rugby masel. S'a fuckin poofs game if ye ask me. Dinnae ken how any cunt kin watch that fuckin shite. It's true though, it's aw fuckin queers thit play that game.

Yir no a poof ur ye mate?

Whit d'ye mean leave um? Jist askin the boy if ehs a poof or no. Simple fuckin question. Mibee the cunt is, mibee eh isnae.

Whaire's it ye come fae mate?

Marchmont!

Hi Skanko, the boy's fi Marchmont.

Big hooses up thaire mate. Bet you've goat plenty fuckin poppy.

Naw? Bit ye stey in a big hoose bit.

No that fuckin big!

No that fuckin big, eh sais!

You stey in a fuckin castle!

D'ye hear the cunt? No that fuckin big.

Whit's it ye dae mate, ye wurkin?

Aye, fuckin right ya cunt!

Aye... bit whit dis that make ye? Whit's it make ye whin yir finished?

A fuckin Accountint!

Hear that Skanko! SKANKO! C'mere the now. C'MERE THE NOW YA CUNT! Boy's an Accountint.

Eh? What the fuck you sayin?

Aye right.

Well, a trainee Accountint.

Trainee Accountint, Accountint, same fuckin thing. Tons ay fuckin hireys.

Naw.

Naw, the boy isnae a poof.

Ah jist thoat that mate, ken wi you bein intae the rugby n that.

Ye goat a burd mate?

Eh?

Thoat ye sais ye wirnae a poof. Ivir hud a ride?

Whit d'ye mean leave the cunt? Jist askin a simple question.

Ivir hud a ride mate?

Either ye huv or ye huvnae. Jist a fuckin question. Ye dinnae huv tae git a beamer.

That's awright then.

Jist a question, see.

Jist wi you bein intae the rugby, ken.

That's ma burd ower thaire.

HI KIRSTY! AWRIGHT DOLL! Be ower in a minute. Jist huvin a wee blether wi ma mate here likesay.

No bad eh? Tidy, eh?

Eh! You fancy ma burd ya dirty cunt?

Eh! You tryin tae say ma burd's a fuckin hound? You tryin tae git fuckin wide?

Naw?

Jist is well fir you ya cunt.

So ye like the rugby, eh? Fitba's ma game. Ah nivir go bit. Barred fae the fuckin groond. Anywey, fitba's fuckin borin shite n aw. Dinnae huv tae go tae the game. Maist ay the action takes place before n eftir the game. Heard ay the Hibs Boys? The CCS? Aye?

Take the swedgin oot ay fitba, it's fuckin deid.

Goan gies a song mate. One ay they poof songs ye sing in the rugby clubs before yis aw shag each other.

Jist a wee fuckin song then cunt!

Jist askin the boy tae gies a fuckin song. Nae hassle likes.

Gies a song mate. C'Moan.

EH! SHUT UP WI THAT SHITE! Flower ay fuckin Scotlin. Shite! Ah hate that fuckin song: Oh flow-ir-ay- Scot-lin… fuckin pish. Gie's a real song. Sing Distant Drums.

Whit dae ye mean leave um? Ahm jist askin the cunt tae sing. Distant Drums.

Eh?

Ye dinnae ken Distant fuckin Drums? No? Listen tae me mate, ah'll fuckin sing it.

I HEAR THE SOUND
DUH-DUH-DUH-DUH
DUH-DUH-DUH-DUH
OF DIS-TINT DRUMS
DUH-DUH-DUH-DUH-
DUH-DUH-DUH-DUH-

SING YA CUNT!

I hear the sound of distant drums. It's easy. Your the cunt wi degrees n that. Ye kin understand that. I-HEAR-THE-SOUND-OF-DISTANT-DRUMS.

That's better, hi, hi, hi.

Skanko! Kirsty! Hear the cunt! Distint fuckin Drums!

Barry. Right. Mine's a boatil ay Becks mate. The mate n aw. The burds ur oan Diamond White's. That's Leanne, Skanko thaire's burd, ken?

Cheers mate.

See Skanko, the cunt's awright. Sound fuckin mate ay mines, by the way.

Whit did ye say yir name wis mate?

Allister, right.

That's fi Allister.

Cheers mate.

S'at you away now mate? Eh? See ye then.

Distant Drums, eh mate!

What a fuckin nondy cunt! Hud the daft cunt singing that auld song.

Distant fuckin Drums, ya cunt.

Beck's then Skanko. Jist cause ay the boy gittin yin, disnae mean tae say you dinnae need tae. Short airms n deep poackits this cunt, eh Leanne?

Cheers. Tae rugby cunts. Fuckin poofs, bit here's tae thum.

Brian Whittingham

DEAR ME

Sorry it's been so long
since I dropped you
a note,
I've been busy at work
and things,
and really did mean
to get in touch
before now.

Since we've been friends
on and off, for
all these years,
I feel the need
to share a word or two,
if you can spare the time.

We should be able
to talk now
without the insecurity
of youth.

With girls,
I know
I didn't help much,
but I was unsure

and, like you,
felt uneasy with crowds
and happier
on my own.

Sorry, but
I didn't realise
that winkle pickers
and the ability to
swear and smoke
and actually be able to *talk*
to a girl!

weren't really such
a big deal,
or I'd have
saved you the bother.

Though when you started work
you did learn how to
swear properly

and *talk* about
getting your hole,
which, in retrospect,
was,   a start
I suppose.

There was a lot
of wasted time,
trying to
tie Windsor knots
and endeavouring to
have your hair
like the photographs
in the hairdressers

and trying painfully hard
to be someone
you could never be.

Though sometimes
you surprised
even me,
like the time you had
a square-go
with the guy who kicked
you in the chest,

that was when
you were under the illusion
that you were good
at football.

When we both know
the problem was

Violence scares
the shit out of you.

Looking back,
the years have
flickered past
like a landscape
viewed from a high-speed train,
and I hope
you are surviving, despite

the small stuff.
That's what you always
tell others,

'Don't sweat the small stuff'
you'll say,
then add knowingly
'it's all small stuff'

it gets a laugh,
even though
you are as serious
as one of
your rare smiles.

I know you miss giving
the kids a hug

and tucking them in
at night,
their unconditional
smiles piercing

and you miss
sending them to sleep
by singing
'Three Wise Men From Carntyne'
as you shoogle the bed.

So I sometimes
think of you
when I am out walking,
or at work
discussing some
technical problem,
or lying on top of the bed

and how easily
you seem to screw up
special relationships

then I feel
the tears
fill my inside
like the cartoon
character who drank
too much water.

But, when I think
of a brother
whom I never took the time
to get to know,

and a Mother who
didn't recognise me
before her pain subdued.

And a Father
who lives alone
and has elevated
complaining about life
to an art form.

Then I reckon
we should savour
living and words and humour,
and shouldn't rubbish others
to distinguish ourselves.

And I still smile
to myself
at the little things
that irritate us

like the coins
in the pocket
that always come out
in the wrong sequence
and you have to
rearrange them so
the largest are
at the bottom,
and the smallest
are at the top

and the two-ply toilet
paper that's tear line
is out of synchronisation

and the fact that
when a carry-out meal
is described as delicious
it invariably isn't

and all the other
things that
cheer us inside
which is important
don't you think?

Anyway

I'll sign off now,

so

don't forget,

Don't sweat the small stuff.

K.M. Windmill

CURRICULUM

I did 'Macbeth' for 'O' Grade English, and
To me the setting was pure Hollywood.
They made all of us learn that Burns was a waster
That if he'd been alive today he'd get banned from
Burger King, and when he was wee he'd have chored sweeties
From the Pic n'Mix. But I thought that I would like a man to
Sing to me on burns without tampons, and with those weeping
Willows and turquoise that later I found were Monet posters.
I could never read Walter Scott, but I could climb his monument.
I'd seen the picture too young, so I would've been bored with
Treasure Island, and anyhow there were no nudie bits in the book
That weren't in the fillem, not like Jaws.
Only the clever ones were told that Burns was a casual
The rest were left with their tits in the dictionary.

They told me that napolean died by decoration
And that hitler melted his snowflake.
They telt me that Jesus was the Son Of God,
They telt me that latin is a deid tongue
And so wis the gaelic
Aye, absolute.

AUNTIE GILL

I used to be 16 and
I didn't ken any better:
George Michael would sing
And I'd believe it was love
And that's how it would taste
To me.
And he was soo hairy and that's
How you spelt 'soO' to mean it
Even more.
And my Modren Studies teacher –
She liked us to call her
Auntie Gill
Because
She came from Townhill
And she'd go to Deacon Blue concerts
And she rated 'Hue & Cry' because
She caught me buying 'Remote' in
Our Price.
And she wasn't married and she had no weans
But her and the other upper hut chicks
Would go for pub lunches in the Roadhouse.